ALL NEW
QUICK
CROSSWORDS

Volume 1

The Telegraph

ALL NEW QUICK CROSSWORDS

Volume 1

hamlyn

An Hachette UK Company
www.hachette.co.uk

First published in Great Britain in 2012 by
Hamlyn, a division of Octopus Publishing Group Ltd
Endeavour House, 189 Shaftesbury Avenue
London WC2H 8JY
www.octopusbooks.co.uk

ISBN 978-0-60062-501-8

A CIP catalogue record for this book is available from the British Library.

Printed and bound by CPI Group (UK) Ltd, Croydon, CR0 4YY

1 3 5 7 9 10 8 6 4 2

Acknowledgements
Telegraph Puzzle Editor: Philip McNeill
Editorial Director: Trevor Davies
Senior Editor: Leanne Bryan
Designer: Eoghan O'Brien
Editorial Assistant: Pauline Bache
Page make up: Dorchester Typesetting Group Ltd
Production: Peter Hunt

EDITOR'S NOTE

Welcome to our new collection of Quick Crosswords. There's no better way to sharpen your wits and widen your vocabulary than to undertake a good Quick Crossword, and we introduce 150 of them here.

Each day in *The Daily Telegraph*, a different compiler sets the Cryptic and Quick crosswords as a pair. This helps to give the puzzles variety as the week goes by, and it should offer a mixture of styles as you work your way through this book.

One thing to look out for is the pun at the start of each puzzle. The first two answers (or sometimes the first three, four or five answers) produce a pun — and the more corny the pun, the better. For instance, if the first two answers are 'Kin' and 'Crustacean', the pun is 'King's Cross Station'. The puns are revealed along with the answers at the back of the book.

This volume happens to include the most famous pun we've ever run in the *Telegraph* — you'll find it in puzzle 23. That particular crossword was compiled by the late Steve Race, the radio and television presenter, who set the Monday Quick crossword for 11 years. Steve's classic pun, which runs to six answers, is a very funny joke — unless you happen to live a certain Midlands town. You'll see why when you tackle it.

Happy solving from everyone in the *Telegraph* crossword team.

Phil McNeill
Telegraph Crossword Editor

Puzzles

The Telegraph

1

Across

1 Scrape (5)
4 – Fitzgerald (4)
8 Expression of surprise (3)
9 Onlooker (9)
10 Row (4)
11 US state (8)
12 Tree (3)
13 Serviette (6)
14 Black Sea port (6)
16 Owing (3)
17 Girl's name (8)
18 Reared (4)
20 Marvellous (9)
21 Racket (3)
22 Daze (4)
23 Greek island (5)

Down

1 First man in space (7)
2 Breathtaking (3-9)
3 Simple (4)
4 City in Devon (6)
5 Leeway (8)
6 Town near Sheffield (12)
7 Wear (4)
11 Relatives (3)
12 Thread-like object (8)
14 Not at home (3)
15 At a moderately slow tempo (7)
16 Deprive of hearing (6)
17 Cuts grass (4)
19 Alliance (4)

Across

1 First musical note (3)
3 Ant's TV partner (3)
5 Aromatic plant (5)
8 Hellenic (5)
9 Detached areas (7)
10 Ballet skirt (4)
11 Lack (8)
13 Fastened clothing (6)
14 Very toxic poison (6)
17 Bicker (8)
19 Birmingham (informal) (4)
22 Warship (7)
23 Plant hormone (5)
24 Strengthened (5)
25 Decline (3)
26 24 hours (3)

Down

1 Finger (5)
2 Last drop in glass (7)
3 Amphibious vehicle (4)
4 Pretentious (6)
5 Very sensitive (8)
6 Old region in Asia Minor (5)
7 Earnest (anag.) (7)
12 Part of a piano (8)
13 Full of relish (7)
15 Photocopied (7)
16 Arm covering (6)
18 League (5)
20 Scabby (5)
21 Doorpost (4)

3

Across

1 Fluid motion (4)
3 Lever on boat (6)
9 Relations (7)
10 Theme (5)
11 Massage (3)
12 Like a towel (9)
13 Artificial (6)
14 Follow-on book (6)
16 Moving apart (9)
19 Pencil of light (3)
21 Farewell (5)
22 Native of Oxford (University) (7)
23 Boil (6)
24 Headland (4)

Down

1 Holy man (5)
2 Public vehicle (7)
4 Exclamation (12)
5 Momentary mistake (5)
6 Musical performance (7)
7 Significant discovery (12)
8 Poems (4)
13 Makes lovable (7)
15 Country in SE Europe (7)
17 Ability to speak (5)
18 Asteroid (4)
20 Americans; pulls (5)

4

Across

1 Ds (4)
4 Select (4)
8 Cain's brother (4)
9 Emotionally shocking (9)
11 Volley (anag.) (6)
13 Shred (7)
15 Protozoan (6)
16 Eye inflammation (6)
18 Stimulus (6)
20 Far (6)
22 New Zealand port (7)
23 Waste matter (6)
25 High-spirited (9)
26 Penalty (4)
27 Leg-pull (4)
28 Robe (4)

Down

2 OT priest (4)
3 Old-fashioned (6)
4 3 down (6)
5 Pepper (6)
6 Protest (9)
7 Sticky earth (4)
10 Compelled (7)
12 Gamin (4)
13 Next after (9)
14 Shorten (7)
17 Try to find (4)
19 American Indian village (6)
20 Responsive (6)
21 Mingling (6)
23 Mild (4)
24 Afresh (4)

5

Across
1 Approve; be fond of (4)
4 Centre of wheel (3)
6 Paddington or Yogi (4)
8 Decay (6)
9 Grew furious (3,3)
10 Cod steak (anag.) (8)
11 – Madrid FC (4)
12 Revolving pebbles (7,6)
17 Bung (4)
19 Large orchestral piece (8)
22 Play it again ! (6)
23 Nile battle hero (6)
24 Plunder (4)
25 Plaything (3)
26 Lewes's river (4)

Down
2 e.g. Dostoevski's Myshkin (5)
3 Moral (7)
4 Hengist and – (5)
5 Street musicians (7)
6 Arbour (5)
7 Mean; typical (7)
10 Knight's prefix (3)
13 Virginia Woolf novel (7)
14 Not a problem (colloq.) (2,5)
15 The Moor of Venice (7)
16 Secret agent (3)
18 Hamlet's spectral father (5)
20 Dosh (5)
21 Recesses (5)

Across

1 Town in NW England (5)
4 Put on the scales (5)
8 Frozen water (3)
9 Liqueur (11)
10 Sanction (7)
12 City in Florida (5)
13 Hit (6)
14 Flowering tree (6)
17 Dentine (5)
19 Happy and carefree (7)
21 Objects connected with famous people (11)
23 & 24 1 across, 4 across, for example (3,5)
25 Era (5)

Down

1 North African country (5)
2 Public house (3)
3 Food fish (7)
4 Evil (6)
5 Mode of expression (5)
6 Pecking order (9)
7 Exact copy (7)
11 Artiste (9)
13 Copse (7)
15 Personal character (7)
16 Fee (6)
18 Delicious (5)
20 S Wales town (5)
22 Zodiac sign (3)

The Telegraph

7

Across

1 Ponderous (5)
4 Squandered (6)
9 Fine cotton (7)
10 French river (5)
11 Orient (4)
12 Vanity (7)
13 By way of (3)
14 Wise men (4)
16 Mess (4)
18 Affirmative (3)
20 Reproach (7)
21 Ordered (4)
24 Argument (3-2)
25 e.g. Bishop (7)
26 Quietened (6)
27 Young mare (5)

Down

1 Dash (6)
2 Tapestry (5)
3 Chinese currency (4)
5 Bitter liqueur (8)
6 Arm muscle (7)
7 Compostion for two (6)
8 Holy city (5)
13 Oral exam (4,4)
15 Strawberry-tree (7)
17 Coup d'état (6)
18 Proficient (5)
19 Heterodoxy (6)
22 Profit (5)
23 Complaint; muscle (4)

8

Across

1 Of sound mind (4)
3 Domicile (4)
6 Raw mineral (3)
9 Traditional building material (6,3,4)
10 Nasal cavities (8)
12 Fibber (4)
13 Consume (3)
15 Humble (6)
18 Part of eye (6)
19 Summit (3)
21 Clothed (4)
22 Caution (8)
25 Denoting a question (13)
26 Objective (3)
27 Purchases (4)
28 Matted fabric (4)

Down

1 Sempstress's essential aid (6 7)
2 Paper money (5)
4 Prophet (6)
5 Whirlpool (4)
6 Long speech (7)
7 Shame (13)
8 Flower arranger (7)
11 Pouch (3)
14 Of interest at the present time (7)
16 Sketched (plan) (7)
17 Pull (3)
20 Mockery (6)
23 The cream (5)
24 Cot (4)

9

Across

1 Officer (7)
8 Suit of cards (6)
9 Seamy (7)
11 Shift (8)
12 Wild ox (5)
14 Small particle (4)
15 French beans (8)
17 Ape (8)
18 – Klemperer, conductor (4)
20 – Howatch, novelist (5)
21 Substance inducing negative reaction (8)
23 Spread out (7)
24 Prayer (6)
25 Fabric (7)

Down

2 Pronounce innocent (6)
3 Jewish greeting (6)
4 Very keen (4)
5 German city (7)
6 Eruptions (9)
7 Slur (9)
10 Refused to acknowledge (9)
12 Fundamentally (9)
13 Party-going celeb (9)
16 Discordant (7)
18 Set of clothing (6)
19 Slates (anag.) (6)
22 Pleasing (4)

Across

1 Cephas (5)
4 Deserves (6)
9 Scottish borough (5)
10 Afternoon performance (7)
11 Connection (7)
12 Force (5)
14 Everything (3)
15 Cloth measure (3)
16 Unwell (3)
18 Snow blade (3)
21 Ocean (anag.) (5)
22 French port (2,5)
23 Small songbird (4,3)
25 S (5)
26 Continent (6)
27 Located (5)

Down

1 Smooth stone (6)
2 Waterproof (9)
3 Reuse (6)
5 Necessitate (6)
6 Electrically charged particle (3)
7 Proper (6)
8 Responsiveness (11)
13 Athletic event (4-5)
17 Australian wattle (6)
18 Putrid (6)
19 Essay (6)
20 Way (6)
24 Atmosphere (3)

11

Across

1 Twist and squeeze dry (5,3)
8 Passed the time (away) (6)
9 Bathing beauties (6)
10 Octopus feeler (8)
11 Vaccination pioneer (6)
13 Coffee (8)
17 Sex meter (anag.) (8)
20 Revenue (6)
23 Escape (5,3)
25 Set alight (6)
26 Cuts off (6)
27 Victorian Poet Laureate (8)

Down

2 Ruff's mate (5)
3 Stocking (5)
4 A monster (anag.) (2-6)
5 e.g. Pollux (4)
6 Penzance marauder ? (6)
7 Orson − (6)
11 'Hey −' (Beatles) (4)
12 Tidy (4)
14 Attitude, job (8)
15 Tolerable (2-2)
16 Eye lecherously (4)
18 Persian King (6)
19 '−, I married him' (Jane Eyre) (6)
21 Shrewd (5)
22 Cracker slip (5)
24 Eject (4)

Across

1 Girl's name (6)
4 Gorse (5)
8 Critical (5)
9 Shining (7)
10 Conjugal (7)
11 Cowshed (4)
12 Stage (3)
14 Abundant supply (4)
15 In addition (4)
18 Large ox (3)
21 African country (4)
23 Occupy (7)
25 Flood (7)
26 Lift (5)
27 Useful (5)
28 Commercial (6)

Down

1 Unpleasantly sticky (6)
2 Impartial (7)
3 Name (8)
4 Lose colour (4)
5 Prepared (5)
6 Respect (6)
7 Restaurant (5)
13 Collected (8)
16 Unparalleled (7)
17 Whisky (6)
19 Pool of money (5)
20 Thoroughfare (6)
22 Pinny (5)
24 Tax (4)

13

Across
4 Flatfish (6)
7 Venues (8)
8 Italian island (6)
10 Adored (7)
11 Genuine (4)
13 Unworried (8)
14 Minus (4)
16 Greek cheese (4)
18 Staunch Tory (4,4)
19 Riotous revel (4)
21 Generating (7)
22 Place of worship (6)
24 Seasickness (3,2,3)
25 Carriage (6)

Down
1 Apostate (8)
2 Rower nearest stern (6,3)
3 Moral rectitude (9)
4 Greek letter (3)
5 Breathe in (6)
6 Glorifies (6)
9 Diocese; observe (3)
11 Trustworthy (9)
12 Arab's tale (anag.) (9)
15 Misspend (8)
16 Conventional (6)
17 Alarm-bell (6)
20 Large antelope (3)
23 Flightless bird (3)

Across

1 High-rated tennis player (4)
3 Pile (4)
9 Stratum (5)
10 Large reptile (9)
11 Bother (5)
12 Precipitation (9)
15 Calibrating (6)
17 Look up to (6)
19 Instrumentalists (9)
21 Scour (5)
23 Altitude (9)
24 Tall structure (5)
25 Place (4)
26 Secondhand (4)

Down

1 Financial protection (8)
2 Feelings (8)
4 Newspaper boss (6)
5 Delighted (7)
6 Religious song (4)
7 Quarry (4)
8 Precious metal (4)
13 Prayers (8)
14 Argued logically (8)
16 Fourth book of the Bible (7)
18 Agreement (6)
20 Applaud (4)
21 Poses (4)
22 Tiers (4)

15

Across

1 Cat's noise (4)
4 Oscillated (6)
7 Slippery fish (3)
9 Meat (4)
10 Teacher (8)
11 Anger (3)
12 Whirl (4)
13 A repulse (anag.) (8)
16 Paris landmark (3,2,8)
19 Nobleman (8)
23 Joke (4)
24 Also (3)
25 Figure of speech (8)
26 500 sheets of paper (4)
27 Monster (3)
28 Superfluous (French) (2,4)
29 Declare (4)

Down

2 Not censored (of books) (12)
3 Elegant (7)
4 Slumber (5)
5 Sky blue (5)
6 Tests (5)
8 The press (6,6)
14 Early birds (5)
15 In the past (3)
17 Flightless bird (3)
18 Largest of the Balearic Islands (7)
20 Tremble (5)
21 Volatile liquid (5)
22 Display of temper (5)

The Telegraph

16

Across

4 Advertised (6)
5 – -a-ling (4)
7 Association (7)
10 Viand (anag.) (5)
11 Towed vehicle (7)
12 Punctuation mark (5)
14 Weakly sentimental (7)
15 Bluish-green tweed (5)
16 Racing tout (7)
20 Upper room (5)
21 Capital of Nova Scotia (7)
22 Broad (4)
23 Anoint (anag.) (6)

Down

1 Pigtail (5)
2 Greek D (5)
3 Crude metal (3-4)
4 Paperback (4)
6 Metric weight (6)
8 Unreliable (7)
9 Jewish language (7)
10 Unit of sound (7)
13 Be servile (6)
14 Waltzing – (7)
17 West Country river (5)
18 Stiff (5)
19 Sunrise (4)

17

Across

1 Well-behaved (4)
3 Lamenting (8)
9 Once more (5)
10 May dons (anag.) (7)
11 Hearing organ (3)
13 'You'll Never –', Kop chant (4,5)
14 Attack (6)
16 Movie awards (6)
18 Dance music in 23 26 (5,4)
20 Donkey (3)
22 Leading to decay (7)
23 Graces, Magi or Blind Mice (5)
25 Vocal gathering (8)
26 IV (4)

Down

1 Solemn (5)
2 Eggs (3)
4 Gilt ware (6)
5 Take-off strips (7)
6 Person beloved (9)
7 e.g. John, Mark (7)
8 Once more (4)
12 Disgust (9)
14 War's din (anag.) (7)
15 Nod (4,3)
17 xxx (6)
19 Chews (4)
21 Young ox (5)
24 – de Janeiro (3)

The Telegraph

18

Across

1 Squandered (4)
3 Extending far (4)
9 Markers at sea (5)
10 Disco (9)
11 Vex (5)
12 Formal meeting (9)
15 Braying sound (6)
17 Young swan (6)
19 The highest level (3,6)
21 Figure out (5)
23 Zoo (9)
24 Inexpensive (5)
25 Ballet skirt (4)
26 Rotate (4)

Down

1 Tea party (8)
2 Number (8)
4 Studded (6)
5 Recede (3,4)
6 Formal dress (4)
7 Catch sight of (4)
8 Agitate (4)
13 Early spring flower (8)
14 Caviar fish (8)
16 Try (7)
18 Musical instrument (6)
20 Fury (4)
21 Dismiss (4)
22 Vegetable (4)

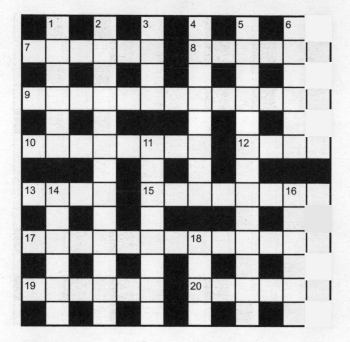

Across

7 Showed contempt (6)
8 Prophecy (6)
9 Gain an advantage over (5,1,5,2)
10 Prattled (8)
12 Final passage (4)
13 Symbol (4)
15 Stronghold (8)
17 Defensive coastal building (8,5)
19 Bar (6)
20 Shed (4-2)

Down

1 Small restaurant (6)
2 Murder of a prominent person (13)
3 Notion (4)
4 Straining pan (8)
5 Army rank (5,8)
6 Nutlike seed (6)
11 Trivial (8)
14 Neckerchief (6)
16 Afternoon nap (6)
18 Norwegian capital (4)

Across
1 Purchases (4)
4 Infirm (4)
8 Drag (4)
9 Speaking two languages (9)
11 Abrupt (6)
13 Mail deliverers (7)
15 Body of singers (6)
16 Instruct (6)
18 Origin (6)
20 Rue (6)
22 Revealed (7)
23 Satellite of a sun (6)
25 Judgements (9)
26 Overt (4)
27 Appends (4)
28 States (4)

Down
2 A single undivided whole (4)
3 A man who courts (6)
4 Tourist attractions (6)
5 Pursues (6)
6 A stiff thick paper (9)
7 Scheme (4)
10 Midday meals (7)
12 Behaves (4)
13 Inhabited (9)
14 Reach a goal (7)
17 Delayed (4)
19 Stretch (6)
20 Small songbirds (6)
21 A natural talent (6)
23 Impoverished (4)
24 Feeling of grudging admiration (4)

21

Across

1 Tomato sauce (7)
5 Subsequent (5)
8 Clerk keeping records (5)
9 – mechanics (physics) (7)
10 Move forward (7)
11 Reside (5)
12 Merry (6)
14 Mollusc (6)
17 African country (5)
19 Regains (7)
22 Teaching (7)
23 Banished person (5)
24 Process of improving equipment (5)
25 Muslim veil (7)

Down

1 Czech novelist (5)
2 Israeli city (3,4)
3 Wading bird (5)
4 Card game for two (6)
5 29 February (4,3)
6 Levy of a tenth (5)
7 Country walker (7)
12 Caretaker (7)
13 Emergency action by planes (7)
15 Holiday business (7)
16 Agitation (6)
18 Great sorrow (5)
20 Board game (5)
21 Telltale (5)

The Telegraph

Across

1 Airborne soldier (4)
4 Small cubes (4)
8 Missing (4)
9 Draftee (9)
11 Net for catching long fish (3-3)
13 Disconnect (7)
15 & 16 Bucks new town (6,6)
18 Craving (6)
20 Welcome (6)
22 Attunes (anag.) (7)
23 Razor (6)
25 Sockeye (3,6)
26 Chimney (4)
27 Gospel writer (4)
28 Moral obligation (4)

Down

2 Stratford's river (4)
3 Away (6)
4 Australian city (6)
5 1/100th of a rouble (6)
6 Venomous (9)
7 Ignore correction (4)
10 Capital of Iran (7)
12 Give out (4)
13 Final offer (9)
14 Gun-case (7)
17 Hut (4)
19 Shipworm (6)
20 – and Delilah (6)
21 Soothed (6)
23 Secure (4)
24 Bard (4)

23

Across

1 Suicidal rodent (7)
5 Heavy weights (4)
7 – Hilton (celeb) (5)
8 In truth (6)
10 Cheerless (4)
11 Chivalrous (8)
13 Save (6)
14 Punctual (2,4)
17 e.g. McGonagall (8)
19 Heavenly body (4)
21 Water Music composer (6)
22 Boundary (5)
23 Lion's den (4)
24 Kitchen sideboard (7)

Down

1 Expert on gems (10)
2 Glass alleys (7)
3 – facto (Latin) (4)
4 – -by-Sea, Sussex (6)
5 Gnat wing (anag.) (8)
6 Upper Nile inhabitant (5)
9 Pretty wire (anag.) (10)
12 Not the favourite (8)
15 e.g. Corinth (7)
16 Wan (6)
18 44th US President (5)
20 Hint (4)

Across

1 Bill of exchange (6)
5 Hungarian composer (5)
9 Have affairs (9)
10 Enquire (3)
11 Bashful (3)
12 A soft blue cheese (9)
14 Venomous snake (3)
16 Minimum (5)
18 Owed as a debt (3)
19 Athletic contest (9)
21 Abraham's nephew (OT) (3)
22 Vegetable (3)
23 Racquet sport (9)
25 Lowest point (5)
26 Peril (6)

Down

2 Perilous (5)
3 Argument (7)
4 Finish (3)
5 Dig (5)
6 Shellfish etc. (7)
7 Give evidence (4,3,5)
8 Spotless (5-3-4)
13 Game bird (5)
15 Diving duck (7)
17 Stress (7)
20 Rome's river (5)
21 Supple (5)
24 Counterfeit (3)

25

Across

1 English novelist (5)
4 Reasonable (4)
8 Small amount (3)
9 Remarkable things (9)
10 Peer (4)
11 Precise (8)
12 Draw (3)
13 Dish under cup (6)
14 Unwell (6)
16 Fool (3)
17 Front of a ship (8)
18 Stand for a coffin (4)
20 One working with money (9)
21 Tool (3)
22 Ancient instrument (4)
23 Religious depiction (5)

Down

1 Testimony (7)
2 Emotion beneath apparent feeling (12)
3 Excessive publicity (4)
4 Charge exorbitantly (6)
5 Native American people (8)
6 Bring back into good condition (12)
7 Friend (4)
11 Manner (3)
12 Inclination (8)
14 Request (3)
15 African ape (7)
16 Nimble (6)
17 Small flute (4)
19 Journey (4)

Across

1 Elevated (4)
4 The former Mesopotamia (4)
8 Wharf (4)
9 Scrumptious (9)
11 Work stoppage (6)
13 Protection (7)
15 A baby's toy (6)
16 Split in two (6)
18 Lofts (6)
20 Carrier (6)
22 Needing moisture (7)
23 A season (6)
25 Extinct reptiles (9)
26 Hostelries (4)
27 Disorder (4)
28 Firing oven (4)

Down

2 Thought (4)
3 Altitude (6)
4 Spear of ice (6)
5 Tickled (6)
6 Functioning in a supporting capacity (9)
7 Sort (4)
10 Persist (anag.) (7)
12 Region (4)
13 Assertion (9)
14 Voted in (7)
17 Makes a mistake (4)
19 Sacred place (6)
20 Sweepers (6)
21 Assault (6)
23 Slender (4)
24 Spoken (4)

The Telegraph

27

Across

1 Gather for harvest (4)
3 London borough (6)
9 Salad plant (7)
10 Drink from apples (5)
11 Rod for snooker (3)
12 e.g. Someone from Islamabad (9)
13 Gentle wind (6)
14 From Paris possibly (6)
16 Cites incorrectly (9)
19 Annoy (3)
21 Provide kit for (5)
22 Naughty fairy (7)
23 Decorations using fillings (6)
24 Daybreak (4)

Down

1 Memento (5)
2 Belgian port (7)
4 Female forebears (12)
5 Rain god (5)
6 Adornment (7)
7 Faller from wall (6,6)
8 Sudden pull (4)
13 African river (7)
15 Short work of fiction (7)
17 Part of skeleton (5)
18 Roman garment (4)
20 Inert gas (5)

The Telegraph

Across

1 Cysts (4)
4 Shelter (3)
6 Yorkshire valley (4)
8 Dairy product (6)
9 Plane-tree (6)
10 Opening in stage floor (8)
11 Greek 8 across (4)
12 Road and railway intersection (5-8)
17 50% (4)
19 Outspoken (8)
22 Flowery (6)
23 Sofa (6)
24 Dutch 8 across (4)
25 Flatfish (3)
26 Memorandum (4)

Down

2 Upper air (5)
3 Spire (7)
4 Remain motionless (3,2)
5 Seaport (anag.) (7)
6 Make seem small (5)
7 Depended upon (5,2)
10 Phone number (abbrev.) (3)
13 Empowered (7)
14 Hard 8 across (7)
15 Blue 8 across (7)
16 Intestine (3)
18 Marketplace (5)
20 Troublesome (5)
21 Awkward (5)

29

Across

1 Bills (5)
4 Arachnid (6)
9 David Beckham (abbrev.) (5)
10 'Wouldn't it be – ?' (song) (7)
11 Fogbound (2,1,4)
12 Stair post (5)
14 Cat (slang) (3)
15 – Winehouse (mus.) (3)
16 Aged (3)
18 Nervous twitch (3)
21 More 16 (5)
22 Iowa, the – State (7)
23 Skittle (7)
25 Artless (5)
26 'Love me –' (Presley) (6)
27 Surrender (5)

Down

1 Spool; reel (6)
2 Welcomed with applause (9)
3 Mrs Rembrandt (6)
5 Stone slab (6)
6 Major (German mus.) (3)
7 e.g. William and Harry (6)
8 One-armed bandit (4,7)
13 Lower vine (anag.) US carnivore (9)
17 Bix's instrument (6)
18 Threefold (6)
19 A score (6)
20 Protect (6)
24 Grandmother (abbrev.) (3)

Across

1 Further (4)
3 Forged (8)
9 Stressed (5)
10 Unhelpful (7)
11 Owned (3)
13 Bondage (9)
14 Irritable (6)
16 Repellent (6)
18 Death (9)
20 Amount (3)
22 Noticeable (7)
23 Tag (5)
25 Riches (8)
26 Liberate (4)

Down

1 Contest (5)
2 Sprint (3)
4 Preposterous (6)
5 Conjugal (7)
6 Ecstatic (9)
7 Aridity (7)
8 Pleads (4)
12 Dictate (9)
14 Storm (7)
15 Sky (7)
17 Rubbish (6)
19 Scream (4)
21 Fracas (5)
24 Pub (3)

31

Across

1 Collier (5)
4 Docks (5)
10 Seaside (anag.) (7)
11 Rolls (5)
12 Competition (5)
13 Real (7)
15 Fancy (4)
17 Part with music (5)
19 Airs (5)
22 Cry (4)
25 Order (7)
27 Penetrate (5)
29 Small weight (5)
30 Lived (7)
31 Musical pauses (5)
32 Concur (5)

Down

2 Emanate (5)
3 Flexible (7)
5 Municipal (5)
6 Drowsy (7)
7 Summed up (5)
8 Mantelpiece (5)
9 Embers (5)
14 Comfort (4)
16 Soft feathers (4)
18 Huge (7)
20 Gap (7)
21 Performer (5)
23 Des, e.g. (anag.) (5)
24 Business (5)
26 Bond, e.g. (5)
28 Sir, or madam (5)

Across

1 Native American tribe (5)
4 The Queen of – (biblical) (5)
10 Stress (7)
11 Chucked (5)
12 Freight (5)
13 Overtaking (7)
15 Relax (4)
17 Punctuation mark (5)
19 Musical play (5)
22 Capital of Italy (4)
25 Feign (7)
27 Peer of the realm (5)
29 Fibbing (5)
30 Mythical creature (7)
31 Concur (5)
32 Employing (5)

Down

2 Exclusive to a center (5)
3 Official attire (7)
5 Detests (5)
6 Impediment (7)
7 Tall chimney (5)
8 Breaks in two (5)
9 Catches on (5)
14 Particle (4)
16 Merit (4)
18 Opportunity (7)
20 Writing implements (7)
21 Trance (5)
23 Smell (5)
24 Denims (5)
26 Bird of prey (5)
28 Tan (5)

33

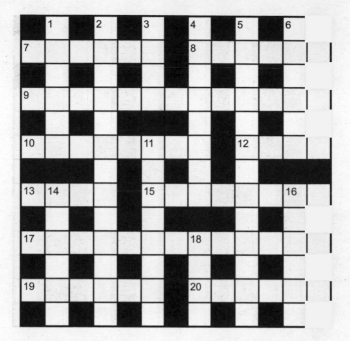

Across

7 Make secure (6)
8 Abhorring (6)
9 Not obligatory (13)
10 Careful (8)
12 American state (4)
13 Fair (4)
15 People seeking retaliation (8)
17 Old apparatus for films (13)
19 Follow-up book (6)
20 Bloke (6)

Down

1 Pacific island (6)
2 Old fogey (5-2-3-3)
3 Joint (4)
4 Agatha – (8)
5 Regular instruction to bank (8,5)
6 Patron saint of Scotland (6)
11 Real base (anag.) (8)
14 For men or women (6)
16 Sword (6)
18 Wild party (4)

The Telegraph

34

Across
1 Front (4)
3 Hovel (5)
7 Orderly (4)
8 Opposition (10)
9 Always (4)
12 Unbearable (11)
13 Obsolete (5)
15 Fling (5)
19 Conjurer (11)
21 Wind (4)
23 Sparkle (10)
24 Elegant (4)
25 Bisect (5)
26 Hence (4)

Down
1 Ominous (10)
2 Chapter (7)
3 Compiler (6)
4 Yearly (6)
5 Genuflect (5)
6 Breaker (4)
10 Swerve (4)
11 Inexorable (10)
14 Rump (4)
16 Acrid (7)
17 Repentant (6)
18 Prick (6)
20 Bloodsucker (5)
22 Twinge (4)

35

Across

1 Fortified wine (4)
5 Scold (4)
7 Largely (anag.) (7)
8 Become smart (6,2)
10 Home of Goliath (4)
12 Repair (4)
14 Know-all (8)
16 Disloyalty (8)
17 Bang (4)
18 Greek god (4)
19 Imagined (8)
22 Open roofed platform (7)
23 – Modern (4)
24 Blow (4)

Down

1 Cat (4)
2 Former union (1,1,1,1)
3 Corridor (8)
4 Seaweed (4)
5 Pasture and fodder plant (3-5)
6 Corrode (4)
9 Go in front (7)
11 Caterer (anag.) (7)
13 Scornful (8)
15 Isocline (anag.) (8)
18 Zing (4)
19 Incidental gain (4)
20 Beehive State (4)
21 Spring flower (informal) (4)

Across
1 Helpful (4)
4 Fire-raising (5)
8 Small crowns (8)
9 Sir – Home (PM 1963) (4)
10 Compassion (4)
11 Irish stout (8)
12 e.g. Easter, Christmas or Rum (6)
14 Me gone (anag.) (6)
16 BBCtv's wide view (8)
19 2009 (Latin) (4)
20 Jeremy – , 16 presenter (4)
21 More surly (8)
22 e.g. Silas Marner (5)
23 Sir's wife (4)

Down
2 Satire (5)
3 Trawled the sea bed (7)
4 Very (Italian mus.) (5)
5 Irish airport (7)
6 Requires (5)
7 Films (6)
13 Shore birds (7)
14 By degrees (7)
15 Over with no runs (6)
17 Self-evident truth (5)
18 Ire (5)
19 Was listless (on a motorbike?) (5)

37

Across

1 Overly (3)
3 Bogus (4)
5 Prejudice (4)
8 Expecting (8)
10 Appendage (4)
11 Scull (3)
13 Gullible (5)
14 Bashful (9)
16 Sorrow (3)
17 Pull (3)
19 Meddle (9)
21 Japes (5)
22 Plan (3)
24 Notion (4)
25 Womanly (8)
26 Cut (4)
27 Surrender (4)
28 Consume (3)

Down

1 Misprint (4)
2 Finished (4)
3 Zealotry (10)
4 Ignite (6)
6 Start (8)
7 Immerse (8)
9 Wireless (5)
12 Undertaking (10)
14 Domicile (8)
15 Brave (8)
18 Civic (5)
20 Steal (6)
22 Colliery (4)
23 Impudent (4)

Across
7 Omitted (6)
8 In pain (6)
10 Rest (3-4)
11 Ghanaian capital (5)
13 Dull (4)
15 Supply (5)
17 Unobserving (5)
19 Heartfelt (4)
23 Gelatinous food (5)
25 Cigar (7)
26 Relish (6)
27 Work (6)

Down
1 Charm (6)
2 Value (6)
3 Wading bird (5)
4 Graze (7)
5 Metal (4)
6 Taj Mahal site (4)
9 Difficulty (4)
12 Narrow elevation (5)
14 Joint (5)
16 Frisky (7)
18 Kiss (4)
20 Unravel (6)
21 Glib talk (6)
22 Precious stone (5)
23 Equitable (4)
24 Not recorded (4)

39

Across

1 Condescend (5)
4 European federal republic (7)
8 Row (3)
9 Desires (5)
10 Relating to vision (7)
11 Enjoyably (10)
14 Latest news (6)
16 Counsel (6)
18 Ensured (10)
22 Illustration (7)
23 Mind (5)
24 Zero (3)
25 Begged (7)
26 Attempt (5)

Down

1 Deluge (8)
2 Insinuation (8)
3 Olfactory organs (5)
4 Terrain (6)
5 Flustered (7)
6 Curved span (4)
7 Scream (4)
12 Laterally (8)
13 Inclination (8)
15 Struck hard (7)
17 Ally (6)
19 Of blue blood (5)
20 Aid (4)
21 Naked (4)

Across

1 Fast-running mammal (4)
3 Wardrobe assistants (8)
9 Snake (5)
10 Feel of fabric (7)
11 British rule in India (3)
13 Fruit (9)
14 Group of relations (6)
16 Emphasise (6)
18 Longing for past (9)
20 Metal (3)
22 Crime against state (7)
23 Fire (5)
25 Church rules (5,3)
26 Watery part of milk (4)

Down

2 Male sheep (3)
4 Eye's membrane (6)
5 Navigational instrument (7)
6 Kit (9)
7 Searchers (7)
8 Improvised accompaniment (4)
12 Film actor (1931–55) (5,4)
14 Extreme enthusiast (7)
15 Communication between groups (7)
17 African country (6)
19 Pulpit (4)
21 Impoverished (5)
24 Tree (3)

41

Across

1 Group of nations (4)
4 Eleventh letter (3)
6 Performed (3)
9 King (3)
10 Scandinavian (5)
11 Taped (anag.) (5)
12 Nursery-rhyme character (4,5)
15 Significant (13)
19 Disappearing (9)
21 Many (prefix) (5)
22 Tripe (5)
24 Small bird (3)
25 London gardens (3)
26 VI (3)
27 Dip (4)

Down

2 Dictionary (7)
3 Military body (5)
4 Relatives (3)
5 Mexican peninsula (7)
6 XII (5)
7 Minced oath (4)
8 Jut out (7)
13 City in northern France (5)
14 Changeable (7)
16 Green-eyed (7)
17 Foolish (7)
18 Permit (5)
20 Vegetable dish (5)
21 Friar (4)
23 Transmit document (3)

Across

1 Leap (5)
4 Tunes (4)
8 Bernstein operetta (7)
9 French capital (5)
10 Exotic Quarter of 9 (5)
11 Fairly slow (mus.) (7)
13 Acute, grave or ^ (6)
15 Showy flower (6)
17 = (La) Manche (7)
20 Austere Greek (5)
22 Cable tower (5)
23 Cricket stroke (2-5)
24 Cricket extras (4)
25 Fear (5)

Down

1 Sung (5)
2 Easily overlooked (12)
3 Versailles palace (7)
4 e.g. O2 (5)
5 Swift (5)
6 Gendarmerie (6,6)
7 Mount (6)
12 Corporal (3)
13 Take on board (6)
14 Tea (French) (3)
16 Dwelt (7)
18 Bill Sikes' girl (5)
19 Tawny big cats (5)
21 Belief (5)

43

Across

1 Alcoholic drink (4)
3 Pranks (6)
9 An intellectual (7)
10 Go round (5)
11 Fasten (3)
12 Highly detailed (9)
13 Umbrella (6)
14 Small stone (6)
16 Dog (9)
19 Burgle (3)
21 Drag (5)
22 Disciple (7)
23 Truthful (6)
24 Tranquil (4)

Down

1 Port in Brittany (5)
2 Spanish painter (2,5)
4 Trumpet-shaped flower (12)
5 Venomous snake (5)
6 Defiant statement (2,5)
7 City near LA (7,5)
8 Notion (4)
13 Enchant (7)
15 Clerical cap (7)
17 Gain knowledge (5)
18 US state (4)
20 Freshwater fish (5)

Across

1 Central part (4)
3 Avoid (4)
9 Tolerate (5)
10 Shopkeeper (9)
11 Massage (5)
12 Criticise severely (9)
15 Mess (6)
17 Girl's name (6)
19 Bargain (9)
21 Map (5)
23 Basic (9)
24 Complete (5)
25 Food (4)
26 Liveliness (4)

Down

1 Underground burial place (8)
2 Musical composition (8)
4 Book of church songs (6)
5 Buff colour (7)
6 Fish (4)
7 Curve (4)
8 Beautiful fairy (4)
13 Stoppered bottle (8)
14 19th-century battle (8)
16 Light (7)
18 Exit (6)
20 Row (4)
21 Brilliant stroke (4)
22 Singer (4)

45

Across

1 Former rulers of Persia (5)
4 Ecologically sound (5)
10 Down payment (7)
11 Presents (5)
12 Italian staple (5)
13 Changed (7)
15 Call (4)
17 Available cash (5)
19 Go red (5)
22 Enthusiastic about (4)
25 Tableland (7)
27 Felt concern (5)
29 Minimal (5)
30 Adroit (7)
31 Catcalls (5)
32 Concur (5)

Down

2 Aspires (5)
3 Spouse (7)
5 Correct (5)
6 Attempts (7)
7 Skilful (5)
8 Mates (anag.) (5)
9 Stage whisper (5)
14 Departed (4)
16 Largest continent (4)
18 Oblivious (7)
20 Securing (7)
21 Suitably (5)
23 Hospital employee (5)
24 Fully-grown (5)
26 Go in (5)
28 Firearm (5)

Across

1 Dagger (4)
4 Less tender (7)
8 Capital of South Carolina (8)
9 Sequence (3)
11 Mingy (6)
13 Time to come (6)
14 Mr Presley (5)
15 Recess (4)
17 Fuel for lorries (4)
18 Decorative coating (5)
20 Wooer (6)
21 Feeling of repeated experience (4,2)
24 Speck (3)
25 Guarantee (8)
26 Reinvigorated (7)
27 Breaking waves (4)

Down

2 Red wine (5)
3 Type of rectangle (6)
4 Pipe (4)
5 Giant planet (6)
6 Hairy (7)
7 Meeting-place (10)
10 Diplomat (10)
12 English composer (5)
13 Demon (5)
16 Type of cheese (7)
18 Conference (native American) (6)
19 People from Dallas? (6)
22 Performer (5)
23 Very dry (4)

47

Across

1 Charge (3)
3 Beats (slang) (5)
6 Tug (3)
8 Freezing (5)
9 East Anglian county (7)
10 9 across town (10)
12 Kernel (3)
15 Vendetta (4)
17 – St Edmunds (4)
18 9 across village (3)
22 It's not hard to miss (4,6)
25 9 across town (7)
26 Do. (5)
27 Lad (3)
28 Genre (anag.) (5)
29 To the – degree (3)

Down

1 Sure to succeed (4-4)
2 Final programme (8)
3 Pod (6)
4 Fidel – (6)
5 Tone down (6)
6 Ancient city (4)
7 Vigil (4)
11 Bath (3)
13 Wolfram (8)
14 Yet he too (anag.) (8)
16 Change colour (3)
19 London borough (6)
20 Litchi (6)
21 Saffron – (6)
23 Branch (4)
24 Children's game (1-3)

Across

1 Japanese play (3)
3 Missouri plateau (5)
6 Gun (anag.) (3)
8 Devon/Cornwall river (5)
9 Worked flour into dough (7)
10 Low vocalist (4,6)
12 Tup (3)
15 Flightless Oz birds (4)
17 Domesticated (4)
18 Fish trap (3)
22 Long-tailed reptiles (10)
25 Diary (7)
26 e.g. 13 and Tits (5)
27 Deer (3)
28 Erik – , French composer (5)
29 Help ! (3)

Down

1 Celebs (8)
2 Plain, rustic (8)
3 Lady Ogre (6)
4 Inquiring (6)
5 Custodian (6)
6 Zeus, Eros and Baal (4)
7 Pakistan language (4)
11 Rodent (3)
13 Ducks (8)
14 Continues (8)
16 Dry (French) (3)
19 Jumbo snouts (6)
20 Small leopard (6)
21 Eatable (6)
23 Partly open (door) (4)
24 Beast of burden (4)

The Telegraph

49

Across

1 Earth (4)
4 Daylight (3)
6 Strike (3)
9 Transgress (3)
10 Alarm (5)
11 Depart (5)
12 Eggplant (9)
15 Tills (4,9)
19 Morose (9)
21 Defence (5)
22 Fetch (5)
24 Curve (3)
25 Utter (3)
26 Moose (3)
27 Reverberation (4)

Down

2 Anthology (7)
3 Outcast (5)
4 Boy (3)
5 Centre (7)
6 Mortal (5)
7 Domesticated (4)
8 Obliquely (7)
13 Bar (5)
14 Soul (7)
16 Ludicrous (7)
17 Obituary (7)
18 Unpredictable (5)
20 Rapscallion (5)
21 Helps (4)
23 Annoy (3)

The Telegraph

Across
1 Arab chief (6)
5 Weapon (5)
9 Retrospection (9)
10 Stick (3)
11 Mole (3)
12 Animal in the Arctic (5,4)
14 Fairy (3)
16 Finger (5)
18 Drink (3)
19 Railway up the side of a mountain (9)
21 Breakfast food (3)
22 Greek letter (3)
23 Bearer of communication (9)
25 Live (5)
26 Vacillate (6)

Down
2 Term of endearment (5)
3 Dull (7)
4 Embrace (3)
5 Greek god of the woodlands (5)
6 Serious (7)
7 She author (5,7)
8 Sofa (12)
13 Lawful (5)
15 Enthusiastic display (7)
17 Stream (7)
20 Humped mammal (5)
21 Bird of prey (5)
24 Sorrowful (3)

The Telegraph

51

Across

1 Salve (4)
4 Assistants (5)
8 Record of names (8)
9 Thought (4)
10 Delayed (4)
11 Gun holders (8)
12 Faculties (6)
14 Extended wellies (6)
16 Administrator of bankrupt firm (8)
19 Receives (4)
20 Matured (4)
21 Performance arenas (8)
22 Of the countryside (5)
23 Examination (4)

Down

2 Get up (5)
3 Equals (7)
4 Pertaining to the ear (5)
5 Wandered (7)
6 Lance (5)
7 Give an account of (6)
13 Slim (7)
14 Most cordial (7)
15 Decayed (6)
17 Enthusiastic (5)
18 Crucial (5)
19 Doors (5)

The Telegraph

52

Across

1 Stage beyond GCSE (1,5)
4 Woodworker's tool (5)
8 Domain (5)
9 Left out (7)
10 Fish tanks (7)
11 Blemish (4)
12 Centre of activity (3)
14 Unwanted plant (4)
15 Mediterranean island (4)
18 Acorn-bearing tree (3)
21 Barred enclosure (4)
23 Imprecise (7)
25 Paper-folding art (7)
26 Saying (5)
27 Prolonged bed rest (3-2)
28 Account of news (6)

Down

1 Disturbance in public place (6)
2 Carry out (7)
3 Fantasy location (2,6)
4 Self-righteous person (4)
5 Old Mexican Indian (5)
6 Put up with (6)
7 Reluctant prophet (5)
13 Drink (8)
16 Bluster (7)
17 Educational institution (6)
19 NZ birds or team (5)
20 Tester (anag.) (6)
22 Appearance (5)
24 Minor chess piece (4)

53

Across

1 Devon river (3)
3 Saucy (4)
5 Effortlessness (4)
8 Go away! (5,3)
10 Equitable (4)
11 Coal-scuttle (3)
13 Gorse (5)
14 Bread-roll (9)
16 Scots racecourse (3)
17 Flying saucer (3)
19 On the contrary (3,4,2)
21 Goodbye (5)
22 Bashful (3)
24 Egg-shaped (4)
25 Mast site (anag.) (8)
26 Corpse (4)
27 Quaint (4)
28 Nap (3)

Down

1 Eat away (4)
2 Ogled (4)
3 Intentional (10)
4 Affair (anag.) (6)
6 Fish-tank (8)
7 Storehouse (8)
9 Truck (5)
12 Unpleasant feeling left behind (10)
14 Burial-place (8)
15 Trainee cleric (8)
18 Combat (5)
20 Survey (6)
22 Large bag (4)
23 Sharp cry (4)

The Telegraph

54

Across

1 Ravine; niche (anag.) (5)
5 Brother's daughter (5)
8 Indian chicken dish (5)
9 Raise (anchor) (5)
10 Vastly (9)
11 Saleroom item (3)
12 Group of helpers (7,4)
15 Computer software (11)
19 And so on (abbrev.) (3)
20 Orbiter (9)
22 Subcontinent (5)
23 Orsino's page (5)
24 Yucky (5)
25 Music for nine (5)

Down

1 Yellow primulas (8)
2 Fools (6)
3 East African republic (8)
4 Hands on hips stance (6)
5 Bread from 22 (4)
6 Decadent (6)
7 Simple (4)
13 Actor (8)
14 Venetian trader (8)
16 Venetian bridge (6)
17 e.g. Hogwarts (6)
18 Not end (anag.) (6)
20 Plunder (slang) (4)
21 Covet (4)

55

Across

1 Chums (7)
5 Test (4)
7 Vista (5)
8 Probability (6)
10 Scintilla (4)
11 Annoyed (8)
13 Powerless (6)
14 Amble (6)
17 Compulsory (8)
19 Festival (4)
21 Pact (6)
22 Play (5)
23 Hint (4)
24 Determine (7)

Down

1 Pugilism (10)
2 Passivity (7)
3 Require (4)
4 Confidential (6)
5 Amount (8)
6 Attract (5)
9 Doctor (10)
12 Last (8)
15 Total (7)
16 Participant (6)
18 Pastoral (5)
20 Reckons (4)

Across

1 Egyptian leader (7)
5 Calm (4)
7 Take exam again (5)
8 Metal (6)
10 Prayer leader (4)
11 Mild (8)
13 Advantageous (6)
14 Feature (6)
17 Breed of dog (8)
19 Sport (4)
21 Unproductive (6)
22 Farewell (5)
23 Bound (4)
24 Explorer (7)

Down

1 Respect (10)
2 Soften (7)
3 Opposed to (4)
4 Bully (6)
5 Coffee (8)
6 Italian city (5)
9 Transparent (3-7)
12 Flatter (6,2)
15 Retired honorary professors (7)
16 Flag (6)
18 No longer fresh (5)
20 Collapse (4)

57

Across

1 One in a religious order (4)
4 Comfort (4)
8 Cry of owl (4)
9 Genre of music (9)
11 Box (6)
13 Middles (7)
15 Ranks in order (6)
16 Sudden attack (6)
18 Lances (6)
20 Comes in (6)
22 Betrothed (7)
23 Track (6)
25 Wire (9)
26 Bequeath (4)
27 Obtains (4)
28 Lease (4)

Down

2 Merely (4)
3 Osculated (6)
4 Subsists (6)
5 Empty areas (6)
6 Held in (9)
7 Astonish (4)
10 Enduring (7)
12 Matures (4)
13 With caution (9)
14 Most approx (7)
17 Simple (4)
19 Cold symptom (6)
20 Consumers (6)
21 Fear (6)
23 Domesticated bovine animals (4)
24 Overt (4)

58

Across

7 Origin (6)
8 Mistakes (6)
10 Peruses again (2-5)
11 Trite (5)
12 Gang (4)
13 Make welcome (5)
17 Candid (5)
18 Nocturnal insect (4)
22 Hungarian composer (5)
23 Unspecified large number (7)
24 Mountaineer's tool (3,3)
25 Cave (6)

Down

1 Flightless bird (7)
2 Fourth part (7)
3 Vast sea (5)
4 Difficulty (7)
5 e.g. Knee (5)
6 Sacred song (5)
9 Space traveller (9)
14 False excuse (7)
15 Originality (7)
16 Irish river (7)
19 Unadorned (5)
20 Guide at wedding (5)
21 Left over (5)

5

59

Across

7 Quarter (6)
8 Maker or repairer (6)
9 Absurd poetry (8,5)
10 Barely sufficient (8)
12 – one's time (4)
13 Quaintly pleasing (4)
15 Witness (6-2)
17 Portable hi-fi (6-7)
19 – State, South Dakota (6)
20 Aero-engine (3-3)

Down

1 Fluctuated (2-4)
2 Interrogate (5-8)
3 Over what period? (4)
4 Pair of tongs (8)
5 It has advantages and disadvantages (5,8)
6 Shaped (anag.) (6)
11 Lily (8)
14 Unfasten (6)
16 Made tea (6)
18 Elevator (4)

60

Across

1 Vintage (French) (3)
3 Red, Black or Tasman (3)
5 Part of speech (4)
7 Lewis Carroll's girl (5)
8 Touch a trout lightly (6)
10 Den (4)
11 e.g. 'Israel in Egypt' (Handel) (8)
13 1951 South Bank spire (6)
14 Mean; squalid (6)
17 Hopeful person (8)
19 Maple (4)
21 Water down (6)
22 e.g. 'Nixon in China' (Adams) (5)
23 Rim (4)
24 e.g. Shylock Ohms (3)
25 Sorrowful (3)

Down

1 1920's dance craze (10)
2 Usefulness (7)
3 Noah's eldest boy (4)
4 Michaelmas daisies (6)
5 Calling (8)
6 'I am the – of the Queen's Navee !' (5)
9 7's new world (10)
12 Sleepy rodent in 9 (8)
15 Duke's wife (7)
16 Please (anag.) (6)
18 Chord of three notes (5)
20 '– River' (song) (4)

61

Across

1 Barb (4)
3 Tunes (4)
9 Stallion (5)
10 Wedlock (9)
11 Bare (5)
12 Truce (9)
15 Saturate (6)
17 Help (6)
19 Curse (9)
21 Bush (5)
23 Clumsy (9)
24 Pursuit (5)
25 Infrequent (4)
26 Legend (4)

Down

1 Killing (8)
2 Obsolete (8)
4 Sardonic (6)
5 Timidity (7)
6 Slog (4)
7 Defunct (4)
8 Frightful (4)
13 Devotion (8)
14 Power (8)
16 Shoemaker (7)
18 Mallet (6)
20 Glimpse (4)
21 Dismiss (4)
22 Stern (4)

Across

1 Twenty-five cents (7)
5 Stand up (4)
7 Penetrate (5)
8 Aspect (6)
10 Pleasant (4)
11 Fetch (8)
13 Latitude (6)
14 Nucleus (6)
17 Nightdress (8)
19 Large fish (4)
21 Peril (6)
22 Accounts' examination (5)
23 Celebrity (4)
24 Ruler (7)

Down

1 Australian state (10)
2 Item (7)
3 Vessel's weight (4)
4 Roof beam (6)
5 Musical instrument (8)
6 Hoard (5)
9 Patron (10)
12 Skive (8)
15 Rumble (7)
16 Edict (6)
18 Bestow (5)
20 Stringed instrument (4)

63

Across

1 Nation (7)
5 Cold-shoulder (4)
7 Itinerary (5)
8 Of milk (6)
10 Brash (4)
11 Pal up with (8)
13 Precious metal (6)
14 Unit of poem (6)
17 Southern Scotland (8)
19 Spoilt kid (4)
21 Car repair shop (6)
22 Cake topping (5)
23 Fair (4)
24 Stabs of pain (7)

Down

1 Without concern (10)
2 Strange (7)
3 Long foot journey (4)
4 Shouted (6)
5 Protection (8)
6 Combine (5)
9 Benefits (10)
12 Apart (8)
15 Caring profession (7)
16 Publicity announcement (6)
18 Aquatic mammal (5)
20 Chinese gooseberry (4)

Across

1 Rambler (5)
4 Staffed (6)
9 Anniversary celebration (7)
10 Thin candle (5)
11 Young cow (4)
12 Need (7)
13 Extinct flightless bird (3)
14 Fencing sword (4)
16 – Fitzgerald (4)
18 Idle talk (3)
20 Fighter in battle (7)
21 Incentive (4)
24 Cloak (5)
25 Win (7)
26 Throne (anag.) (6)
27 Elegance (5)

Down

1 Seizure of vehicle in motion (6)
2 Afghan capital (5)
3 Reign (4)
5 Valuable old objects (8)
6 Of a wedding (7)
7 Coastal county (6)
8 Striped animal (5)
13 Of moderate quality (8)
15 Business associate (7)
17 On/off device (6)
18 Very serious (5)
19 Breakwater (6)
22 Authorised substitute (5)
23 Top cards (4)

65

Across

1 Piece of cutlery (4)
4 Cyclones (4)
8 Confident (4)
9 Certainly not (2,2,5)
11 Ballet- – (6)
13 Greek port (7)
15 Tom –, footballer (6)
16 Art of healing (6)
18 Zodiacal bull (6)
20 Sternutation (6)
22 Temporary substitute (7)
23 Hindu incarnation (6)
25 One's double (9)
26 Straight line (4)
27 Bracken (4)
28 Betting machine (4)

Down

2 African antelope (4)
3 China clay (6)
4 Elbowroom (6)
5 Tease (4,2)
6 Ballroom dance (9)
7 Terror (4)
10 Providing sliding
windowpanes (7)
12 Identikit (1-3)
13 Type of drill (9)
14 Seal fur (anag.) (7)
17 Cook (4)
19 Voters (anag.) (6)
20 Oral (6)
21 Young bird of prey (6)
23 Slightly open (4)
24 Burlesque (4)

Across

1 Trendy (3)
3 Mud wallower (abbrev.) (5)
6 Light beam (3)
8 Shout of approval (5)
9 Pa lover (anag.) (7)
10 Mistrustful (10)
12 Infant food (3)
15 Catch sight of (4)
17 e.g. Force 8 (4)
18 Weep audibly (3)
22 Dracula KGB (anag.) (10)
25 Jane Eyre, 1984 or The Oaks (7)
26 Lurch (anag.) (5)
27 Insane (3)
28 Woolly ruminant (5)
29 Sweet potato (3)

Down

1 Aggressive seller (8)
2 Arm/body exercises (5-3)
3 Epic (6)
4 Financial gain (6)
5 Let me in ! (4,2)
6 Actor's part (4)
7 Golfer's tremor (4)
11 Droop (3)
13 South American country (8)
14 'The Pit and the –' (Poe) (8)
16 Lout (3)
19 Gusts (6)
20 Frozen water (6)
21 Food container (6)
23 Swindle (slang) (4)
24 e.g. Joker (4)

Across

1 Exhale (4)
4 Absent (4)
8 Prod (4)
9 Concession (9)
11 Chevalier (6)
13 Expunged (7)
15 Cask (6)
16 Lookalike (6)
18 Forgive (6)
20 Hope (6)
22 Filthy (7)
23 Snub (6)
25 Incorrect (9)
26 Passable (4)
27 Blister (4)
28 Remove (4)

Down

2 Dormant (4)
3 Vacuum (6)
4 Shingle (6)
5 Pinched (6)
6 Sprite (9)
7 Chair (4)
10 Approve (7)
12 Adept (4)
13 Harsh (9)
14 Relaxation (7)
17 Eternally (4)
19 Vigour (6)
20 Nearly (6)
21 Obvious (6)
23 Symbol (4)
24 Twilight (4)

Across

1 Deceptive move (5)
4 Begs (5)
8 Large deer (3)
9 Matador (11)
10 Brainbox (7)
12 Youngster (5)
13 Ordinary (6)
14 Confer (6)
17 Serious (5)
19 Symbols (7)
21 Explorer (11)
23 Increase (3)
24 Perfect (5)
25 Bumpkin (5)

Down

1 Moral tale (5)
2 Poorly (3)
3 A lustrous silk (7)
4 Buddhist temple (6)
5 Garret (5)
6 Napkin (9)
7 Lake District mountain (7)
11 Loose blouse (9)
13 Bunch of flowers (7)
15 Consulate (7)
16 A herb (6)
18 Variety show (5)
20 Incantation (5)
22 Large tree (3)

69

Across

1 Elevated (4)
3 Move to music (5)
7 Religious adherent (eastern) (4)
8 Sporting dogs (10)
9 Assists (4)
12 Depressions in earth's crust (4,7)
13 Parotid gland disease (5)
15 Perspire (5)
19 Knockout drug (11)
21 Collection of facts (4)
23 Solid ground (5,5)
24 Half a quart (4)
25 Submit (5)
26 Courage (colloq.) (4)

Down

1 Type of spectacles (4-6)
2 Non-convertible car (7)
3 Player of records (6)
4 Goad (6)
5 Attempt (5)
6 Slip (4)
10 Man, for example (4)
11 St Nicholas (5,5)
14 Castle surround (4)
16 Crying (7)
17 Educational qualification (6)
18 Maroon (6)
20 Dapper (5)
22 Opera song (4)

The Telegraph

Across

1 Prohibition (3)
3 Device for lock (3)
5 Satellite (4)
7 Hepatic organ (5)
8 Type of bird (6)
10 50% (4)
11 Peevish (8)
13 Focus more closely (4,2)
14 Small river (6)
17 Firebug (8)
19 Information (4)
21 Place of worship (6)
22 Impromptu (2,3)
23 Rugged cliff (4)
24 Mingle (3)
25 Not bright (3)

Down

1 Doomed feaster in OT (10)
2 Ivor – (7)
3 Pavement's edge (4)
4 Willing conformers (3-3)
5 Blood-sucking insect (8)
6 Spiritualists' board (5)
9 Philatelist's book (5,5)
12 Canadian city (8)
15 Empowered (7)
16 Respect (6)
18 Curse (5)
20 Karl – (4)

71

Across

1 Ripped (4)
4 Leg joint (4)
8 Long wailing cry (4)
9 Wading bird (9)
11 Arm of the Mediterranean (6)
13 Ending (7)
15 (Half of) lower garment (6)
16 Diving bird (6)
18 Finch (6)
20 Ski-race (6)
22 Conjunctivitis (4-3)
23 Expression of irritation (3-3)
25 Lopped (9)
26 Understand (4)
27 Painful (4)
28 Norse poem collection (4)

Down

2 Oh dear (4)
3 Simpleton (6)
4 Nonsense (slang) (6)
5 – Road, Leeds United's ground (6)
6 Tomato (4-5)
7 Scottish valley (4)
10 Readable (7)
12 Wading bird (4)
13 Canoeists (anag.) (9)
14 Back of the head (7)
17 Hindquarters (4)
19 Corrosive acid (6)
20 Bony (6)
21 Lemur (3-3)
23 Yorkshireman (4)
24 Ward off (4)

Across

1 Grind one's teeth (5)
4 Calf's flesh (4)
8 Err (3)
9 Memphis's state (9)
10 On the lam (4)
11 Busyness (8)
12 Mineral (3)
13 Safe (6)
14 Sally Magnusson's father (6)
16 Hastened (3)
17 Esteemed (8)
18 Volcano (4)
20 Lifts (9)
21 Queer (3)
22 King's – , Norfolk (4)
23 Antiquated (5)

Down

1 Chatterers; bagpipe bellows (3,4)
2 King Hal's fourth wife (4,2,6)
3 Pop successes (4)
4 Car-free city (6)
5 Person from 9 (8)
6 Lovers' meetings (12)
7 Exciting (4)
11 Exist (3)
12 Customary (8)
14 Crazed (3)
15 Support (5,2)
16 Fame (6)
17 Dame – Laine (4)
19 Employer (4)

73

Across

1 British coin (5)
5 Characteristic (5)
8 Very fat (5)
9 Complete (5)
10 Awareness (9)
11 Organ of vision (3)
12 Warm-hearted (4-7)
15 Outlay (11)
19 Encountered (3)
20 Maze (9)
22 Ludicrous situation (5)
23 Greek island (5)
24 Effective power (5)
25 West Yorkshire city (5)

Down

1 Caution (8)
2 A spice (6)
3 US siege site (8)
4 Drug (6)
5 Inform (4)
6 Moroccan port (6)
7 Weighty book (4)
13 Honest (8)
14 Anguish (8)
16 Small stone (6)
17 Snub (6)
18 Come out (6)
20 Missing (4)
21 Wealthy (4)

Across

1 Unstimulated (5)
4 Watery discharge (5)
8 Tree (3)
9 Selling to press material for simultaneous publishing (11)
10 Cheat (7)
12 Precise (5)
13 Slender sword (6)
14 Jerk (6)
17 Cancel (5)
19 Edible root (7)
21 Appropriate for the part (2,9)
23 Drink (3)
24 Russian revolutionary (5)
25 Colouring (5)

Down

1 Foundation (5)
2 Manage (3)
3 Lessen (7)
4 Learning book (6)
5 Cream (5)
6 A cocktail (9)
7 Cat renowned for speed (7)
11 Unbiased (9)
13 Italian dish (7)
15 Justify (7)
16 Rick (6)
18 Francis –, Irish painter (5)
20 Clear (5)
22 Yellowish brown (3)

75

Across

1 Symptom of chest infection (5)
4 Minor setbacks (7)
8 Chop (3)
9 Nuisances (5)
10 Assumed (7)
11 Gathering (10)
14 Pact (6)
16 Mature creatures (6)
18 Give as example (10)
22 Holidaymaker (7)
23 Hitch a lift (5)
24 Suffer (3)
25 Administrator (7)
26 Foe (5)

Down

1 Ability to perform or produce (8)
2 Having no answer (8)
3 Rush; urgency (5)
4 Physical welfare (6)
5 Enthroned (7)
6 As far as (2,2)
7 Team (4)
12 Delight (8)
13 Gathering (8)
15 Relating (7)
17 Stringed instrument (6)
19 Legal ownership (5)
20 Stalk (4)
21 Char (4)

Across

1 Shout (4)
3 Discoverer of strait (6)
9 Most considerate (7)
10 Article of food (5)
11 Bone (3)
12 Stalactite (9)
13 Burgeon (6)
14 Disturbance (6)
16 Harmful (9)
19 Sunburn (3)
21 Ooze out (5)
22 Muslim official (7)
23 Hate (6)
24 Insect (4)

Down

1 Bread maker (5)
2 Place of alcoholic refreshment (4,3)
4 Popular American singer (5,7)
5 American state (5)
6 Divine female (7)
7 Main office (12)
8 Needle case (4)
13 Payment for cleric (7)
15 Member of community (7)
17 Combat between knights (5)
18 Units of resistance (4)
20 Piece for nine musicians (5)

77

Across

1 Richard –, Earl of Warwick (7)
8 Room (7)
9 Dame Cleo –, jazz musician (5)
10 Surpass (9)
11 Poem (3)
12 Jockey (5)
13 Disciple (5)
14 Trousers (5)
16 Psalmist (5)
19 Rower (3)
20 During a period, or a Parliamentary paper (9)
22 Hibernian (5)
23 Guitar picks (7)
24 Bitterness (7)

Down

1 Naval commander (6)
2 More conceited (6)
3 Waves running in the wind's direction (3,5)
4 Cream cake (6)
5 Col (4)
6 Grovelling (6)
7 Dealer (6)
13 Park shelter (8)
14 Jesus's earthly father (6)
15 Jane –, authoress (6)
16 Scottish resort (6)
17 Hooded cloak (6)
18 Legendary king (6)
21 Jot (4)

Across

1. Not a soul (2,3)
4. e.g. Pan-pipes (5)
10. Breakfast foods (7)
11. 6am R4 series (5)
12. Follow after (5)
13. Showy shrubs (7)
15. Japanese wrestling (4)
17. Apartments (5)
19. Paunchy (5)
22. Mrs Knightley (4)
25. Daniel – (George Eliot) (7)
27. Rankin's inspector (5)
29. Larry – (harmonica) (5)
30. Kylie (7)
31. Taint (anag.) (5)
32. Corset supports (5)

Down

2. Perfume rootstock (5)
3. Closest (7)
5. No-ball score (5)
6. LA baseball team (7)
7. Performed (5)
8. Indian state (5)
9. Rose Lee musical (5)
14. Enlarging lens (4)
16. Secondhand (4)
18. Rhine siren (7)
20. Not bare (anag.) (7)
21. Perfect (5)
23. Al Jolson's mum (5)
24. Braintree county (5)
26. Bellini opera (5)
28. One over par (5)

79

Across

1 Angrier (6)
4 Keg (4)
9 Transgress (3)
10 Endured (9)
11 Ogling (7)
12 Gripe (5)
13 Doctrine (5)
15 Residue (5)
20 Edict (5)
22 Uncontrolled (7)
24 Meeting (9)
25 Space (3)
26 Woman (4)
27 Myth (6)

Down

1 Humbly (6)
2 Requiem (5)
3 Scholarly (7)
5 Dart (5)
6 Meaningful (7)
7 Saying (5)
8 Sloping edge or chamfer (5)
14 Extremist (7)
16 Contrition (7)
17 Cash (5)
18 Banal (5)
19 Brainless (6)
21 Globular (5)
23 Squabble (5)

Across

1 Ceremonial observances (5)
4 Hard (5)
10 More reasonable (7)
11 Move to music (5)
12 Critically examines (5)
13 School subject (7)
15 Simple (4)
17 Casts off (5)
19 Beasts of burden (5)
22 Ruler (4)
25 Direction finder (7)
27 Lessen (5)
29 Aida, e.g. (5)
30 Good-for-nothing (7)
31 Following (5)
32 Claim (5)

Down

2 Thoughts (5)
3 Unprotected (7)
5 Strangely (5)
6 Real (7)
7 Sharp (5)
8 Encloses (5)
9 Inward feeling (5)
14 Song of worship (4)
16 Questions (4)
18 Flemish (anag.) (7)
20 Least pretty (7)
21 Cruise, e.g. (5)
23 Flow out (5)
24 Fidelity (5)
26 Vigilant (5)
28 Cereal (5)

81

Across
1 Long walk (4)
3 Should (5)
7 Part in film (4)
8 Modelling clay (10)
9 Female relative (4)
12 Trials (11)
13 Sarcasm (5)
15 Bowl (5)
19 Instructive (11)
21 Certain (4)
23 A commissioned officer (10)
24 Couch (4)
25 Cede (5)
26 Skidded (4)

Down
1 Occurrences (10)
2 Oriental (7)
3 Source (6)
4 Profited (6)
5 A nice surprise (5)
6 Scheme (4)
10 Employs (4)
11 Interpreted (10)
14 Finished (4)
16 Quantities (7)
17 Plan (6)
18 Declared (6)
20 Postpone (5)
22 On top of (4)

Across

1 Document cover (6)
4 Opening (4)
9 Army colour (5)
10 American state (7)
11 Prizewinner's decoration (7)
12 Very fat (5)
13 Beano (6)
15 Egyptian god (6)
18 Primate (5)
20 Helps (7)
23 Spectacular ceremony (7)
24 Crouch (5)
25 Fuel from coal (4)
26 Unpowered aircraft (6)

Down

1 Holy man (5)
2 Illicit affair? (7)
3 Expel (5)
5 Having a smell (7)
6 Person dismissed from country (5)
7 Sugary (5)
8 Female monster (6)
13 Ramshackle car (6)
14 Set aside (7)
16 Echo (7)
17 Dance in 3/4 time (5)
19 Conjuror's art (5)
21 Fibre (5)
22 Stringed instrument (5)

5

The Telegraph

83

Across

1 Knight (3)
3 Outfit (3)
5 Heehaw (4)
7 Execration (5)
8 Dull (6)
10 Tramp (4)
11 Exciting (8)
13 Endorse (6)
14 Slipshod person (6)
17 Songbird (8)
19 Malay boat (4)
21 Learned expert (6)
22 Lotto (5)
23 Rotate (4)
24 Dried grass (3)
25 Dolt (3)

Down

1 Sweetener (10)
2 Arbiter (anag.) (7)
3 Fort (4)
4 Equipment (6)
5 Calabrese (8)
6 Viper (5)
9 Shocking (10)
12 Intermittently (3-3-2)
15 Terrace (7)
16 Frustrate (6)
18 Punch (5)
20 Abide by (4)

Across

1 Castrated ram (6)
4 Gain (6)
9 Followers of Guru Nanak (5)
10 Conifer fruit (3-4)
11 Consume (3)
12 Mischa – (violin) (5)
13 Pastoral poem (7)
15 '– Man' (Tammy Wynette) (5,2,4)
19 Warship (7)
20 Crazy (5)
21 Japanese play (3)
22 Cricket stroke (2-5)
24 eg. Otello (5)
25 Various (6)
26 Shire, percheron and palominos (6)

Down

1 Cricket annual (6)
2 Japanese town (9)
3 Ruhr city (5)
5 Pastorally (7)
6 To and – (3)
7 Wobble (6)
8 Fuel injection device (11)
14 Wicket-keeper's gloves (9)
16 Retsina (anag.) (7)
17 Thespians (6)
18 Orbital road (6)
20 Snap (5)
23 College tutor; put on (3)

85

Across
- **4** Fish (6)
- **5** German novelist (4)
- **7** A principality (7)
- **9** Soiled (5)
- **10** Sister (3)
- **11** Snare (3)
- **13** Demonstration (5)
- **15** Surprise (7)
- **16** Farewell (5)
- **17** Weep (3)
- **18** Coffer (3)
- **21** Literary style (5)
- **22** Riotous party (5-2)
- **23** Ballerina's skirt (4)
- **24** Embarrassing failure (6)

Down
- **1** Peer (5)
- **2** Fruit of an oak (5)
- **3** Quality (7)
- **4** Painful emotion (4)
- **6** Idea (6)
- **8** Breach (7)
- **9** Condemn (7)
- **12** Sphere (3)
- **14** Arrival (6)
- **15** Hide (7)
- **18** Iron block (5)
- **19** Borders town (5)
- **20** Sport (4)

Across

1 Additional (4)
4 Way of walking (4)
8 Man-eating giant (4)
9 Elderly (9)
11 Unpleasant experience (6)
13 Absence of sound (7)
15 Straw hat (6)
16 Beefeaters (6)
18 Skilful (6)
20 A pastis (6)
22 Nightclub entertainment (7)
23 Sign (6)
25 Wicked (9)
26 Short skirt (4)
27 Remain (4)
28 Avoid deliberately (4)

Down

2 Finished (4)
3 Draw out (6)
4 Collect (6)
5 Folly (6)
6 Accord (9)
7 Buy and sell (4)
10 Climbing plant (7)
12 Swedish pop group (4)
13 Religious rite (9)
14 Dictionary (7)
17 Naked (4)
19 Flair (6)
20 Pope's office (6)
21 Neglectful (6)
23 Type of house (4)
24 Ballet skirt (4)

Across

1 Ice over (6)
5 Soft fleshy fruit (5)
9 Breaks up (9)
10 Eggs (3)
11 Strange (3)
12 Part of a school (9)
14 Anger (3)
16 Bordered (5)
18 Positive response (3)
19 Optimistically (9)
21 A long way (3)
22 Geological period (3)
23 Electronic pianos (9)
25 Looks after (5)
26 Smaller, more cramped (6)

Down

2 Lassoed (5)
3 Otalgia (7)
4 Consume (3)
5 Mails (5)
6 Excuse (7)
7 School principal (12)
8 Amazement (12)
13 Theatrical backer (5)
15 Elucidate (7)
17 Ship repair area (3,4)
20 Counterfeits (5)
21 Coerce (5)
24 High-pitched bark (3)

Across

1 Pub (3)
3 X (3)
5 Cathedral town? (4)
7 Rather (5)
8 Of exceptional quality (2,4)
10 Thing on list (4)
11 Unexceptional (8)
13 Pastoral poems (6)
14 Glacially cold (6)
17 Protested (8)
19 Bathroom powder (4)
21 Field event (6)
22 North American deer (5)
23 Pile (4)
24 Droop (3)
25 Reserved (3)

Down

1 Ecclesiastical interrogator (10)
2 In an unsophisticated manner (7)
3 Pretty-pretty (4)
4 Poked at (6)
5 Coal mine (8)
6 Poisonous (5)
9 Fussy (10)
12 Warbler (8)
15 Very enthusiastic (7)
16 Population count (6)
18 Sap (5)
20 Self-satisfied (4)

89

Across
1 Through (3)
3 Meadow (3)
5 Ways of walking (5)
8 Unbending (5)
9 Disciple (2,5)
10 Netherworld (4)
11 Separately (3,2,3)
13 Paradise (6)
14 Refinement (6)
17 Of the stars (8)
19 Traditional story (4)
22 Conflagration (7)
23 Seventh 13 across (5)
24 Underworld (5)
25 Craze (3)
26 Hawthorn blossom (3)

Down
1 Scorch (5)
2 Algeria (anag.) (7)
3 Peeress (4)
4 Agree (6)
5 Make widely known (2,6)
6 Nitro (anag.) (5)
7 Witchcraft (7)
12 Serve as a soldier (4,4)
13 Cannabis (7)
15 Blissful place (7)
16 Dismiss temporarily (3,3)
18 Former Welsh county (5)
20 Hoarse (5)
21 Retired (4)

Across

1 Better than war-war (Churchill) (3-3)
4 Orson – (films) (6)
7 Lancs loading-point (5,4)
9 Marquetry (4)
10 Pop; precious stone (4)
11 Hot spicy dish (5)
13 Becomes alert (4,2)
14 Cars (6)
15 Pukka people (6)
17 Wall plaster (6)
19 Old sailors (5)
20 Chat (4)
22 Bargain (4)
23 Flash in the sky (9)
24 Robing-room (6)
25 'Nineteen – Four' (novel) (6)

Down

1 Elephants (6)
2 Clink (4)
3 Be quiet! (4,2)
4 Windscreen cleaners (6)
5 Look lecherously (4)
6 Feeds with fuel (6)
7 Cenotaph street, SW1 (9)
8 Talking extravagantly (9)
11 Restrains (5)
12 W. B. – (Irish poet) (5)
15 Route guide (6)
16 Move ostentatiously (6)
17 Posture; attitude (6)
18 Fish-eating bird (6)
21 Tartan skirt (4)
22 Kiss and cuddle (slang) (4)

91

Across

1 Augur (4)
5 Den (4)
7 Foolish (7)
8 Topple (8)
10 Pant (4)
12 Sect (4)
14 Cask (8)
16 Hoodlum (8)
17 Tack (4)
18 Relish (4)
19 Offender (8)
22 Stunt (7)
23 Across (4)
24 Peak (4)

Down

1 Hairless (4)
2 Apiece (4)
3 Rebound (8)
4 Sagacious (4)
5 Elongate (8)
6 Backside (4)
9 Teach (7)
11 Endurance (7)
13 Jointly (8)
15 Fortress (8)
18 Nothing (4)
19 Cloak (4)
20 Scintilla (4)
21 Tempt (4)

Across

1 Ruler (7)
5 Italian city (4)
7 Snapshot (5)
8 Charts (6)
10 In the same place (4)
11 Do select (anag.) (8)
13 Be forgotten (2,4)
14 Impasse (6)
17 Suave (8)
19 Child of five (4)
21 Immoral behaviour (6)
22 Indian princess (5)
23 Wheel pivot (4)
24 Azure (3-4)

Down

1 Planning route (7,3)
2 Stone artefact (7)
3 Crow-like bird (4)
4 Barter (6)
5 Touring performers (8)
6 Exclamation of surprise (2,3)
9 First couple (4,3,3)
12 A utensil (anag.) (8)
15 Diary (7)
16 Constraint (6)
18 Part of a flower (5)
20 Chafe (4)

93

Across
1 Credence (6)
5 Falls flat (5)
9 Travel documents (9)
10 Check (3)
11 Beam of light (3)
12 Causes to happen (9)
14 Cry of a rook (3)
16 Happening (5)
18 Health resort (3)
19 Reflex (9)
21 Form of humour (3)
22 Anger (3)
23 Yield (9)
25 Horrible (5)
26 Want (6)

Down
2 Attempt (5)
3 Ameliorate (7)
4 Distant (3)
5 Abstains from food (5)
6 Patent (7)
7 Acceptable (12)
8 Gratitude (12)
13 Thorax (5)
15 Spectator (7)
17 Hearts (slang) (7)
20 Hazy (5)
21 Type of long-legged bird (5)
24 Free (of) (3)

Across

1 Wharf (4)
4 Qualities of colour (5)
8 Party following winter sports (5-3)
9 Rodent (4)
10 Fish; low voice (4)
11 Portuguese navigator (8)
12 Comment (6)
14 South American river (6)
16 Belligerent patriotism (8)
19 End of sleeve (4)
20 Leg or arm (4)
21 Job for easy money (8)
22 Mark –, author (5)
23 Underworld river (4)

Down

2 Employers (5)
3 Muslim veil (7)
4 Object (5)
5 Short work of fiction (7)
6 Dance; sauce (5)
7 Drug (6)
13 Branch of maths (7)
14 Man sold (anag.) (7)
15 Ancient university (6)
17 Fool (5)
18 Norwegian playwright (5)
19 Boldly conceited (5)

95

Across

1 Understood (4)
4 Complaint (4)
8 Approach (4)
9 Small berries e.g. (9)
11 Deference (6)
13 Cross-shaped connection (7)
15 Large stain (6)
16 Chest pain (6)
18 Tempt (6)
20 Allot (6)
22 Oppressive (7)
23 Feast (6)
25 Tibia of dressed fowl (9)
26 Stern deck (4)
27 Unfledged hawk (4)
28 Jerk (4)

Down

2 Rule (4)
3 Heavy load (6)
4 Muslim teacher (6)
5 Chest disorder (6)
6 Liver inflammation (9)
7 Itch (4)
10 Unnamed person (2-3-2)
12 Proficient (4)
13 Cognation (anag.) (9)
14 Freezing (3-4)
17 Skin condition (4)
19 Go (6)
20 One of the Three Musketeers (6)
21 Sweltering (6)
23 Stout cord (4)
24 Examine hastily (4)

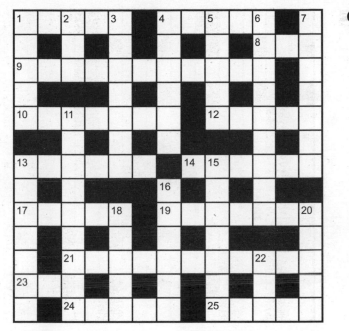

Across

1 Castle ditches (5)
4 Hertfordshire (abbrev.) (5)
8 & 9 'Hail, True Body' (Latin) (3,5,6)
10 Mister (posh) (7)
12 Gown (5)
13 Aspire (anag.) (6)
14 String of beads (6)
17 Essential (5)
19 Draw level (5,2)
21 R.I.P. (4,2,5)
23 Golf peg (3)
24 Challenges (5)
25 Noblemen (5)

Down

1 Film (5)
2 Earth's atmosphere (3)
3 Peaks (7)
4 31st US president; dam; vacuum-cleaner (6)
5 Quick (5)
6 Englishman (derog.) (9)
7 'Clair de Lune' composer (7)
11 Cut into four (9)
13 Need (7)
15 x8 (7)
16 Pilgrims' pouches (6)
18 Intense beam (5)
20 Noblemen (5)
22 Burns county (3)

The Telegraph

97

Across

1 Patrol (4)
4 Course (5)
8 Sanitary (8)
9 Obligation (4)
10 Nimble (4)
11 Frozen food (3,5)
12 Professional terminology (6)
14 Bath sponge (6)
16 Guarantee given to a purchaser (8)
19 Favour (4)
20 Slight quarrel (4)
21 Huge (8)
22 Undressed leather (5)
23 Part of egg (4)

Down

2 Improve morally (5)
3 Strained state (7)
4 Preliminary survey (5)
5 Endure (7)
6 Minor actor (5)
7 Short-sightedness (6)
13 African mammal (7)
14 Faithfulness (7)
15 Socially inept person (6)
17 Assumed name (5)
18 Recess (5)
19 Herb (5)

The Telegraph

Across

7 In instalments (6)
8 Carton (6)
9 Fear of spiders (13)
10 Originate (8)
12 Vegetable (4)
13 Role (4)
15 Cor! Gelly (anag.) – a low-cal sweetener (8)
17 Sanctioning (13)
19 Forsake (6)
20 Spies (6)

Down

1 Eccentric person (6)
2 Details (13)
3 Tribe (4)
4 Fit of infuriation (8)
5 Master (13)
6 Cat-like (6)
11 Disregards (8)
14 Highest point (6)
16 Decorative (6)
18 Not at home (4)

99

Across

1 Alas and – (5)
4 Courage (5)
10 Ore (7)
11 Sum up (5)
12 Shipment (5)
13 Buccaneers (7)
15 Bonded (4)
17 Repast (5)
19 Minimal (5)
22 Regular (4)
25 Result (7)
27 Profundity (5)
29 Flax cloth (5)
30 Of no purpose (7)
31 Read (5)
32 Requested (5)

Down

2 Of the moon (5)
3 Edible roots (7)
5 Mistake (5)
6 Recounts (7)
7 Slap (5)
8 Inclination (5)
9 Muscular contraction (5)
14 Lazy (4)
16 One of a list (4)
18 No longer in existence (7)
20 Eternal (7)
21 Having high moral qualities (5)
23 Goddess of love (5)
24 Stage (5)
26 Possessed (5)
28 A bit of something (5)

Across
1 Cockeyed (4)
3 Jumbled mass (6)
9 Police station (slang) (3,4)
10 Allotment (5)
11 Metal (3)
12 Not temporary (9)
13 Mammal; pester (6)
14 Certainly (6)
16 Extravagantly styled play (9)
19 Unit of work (3)
21 Cut corners (5)
22 File away (7)
23 Restoration author (6)
24 Conduit (4)

Down
1 Racecourse (5)
2 Fretted (7)
4 Familiarity (12)
5 Small wood (5)
6 Demanded (7)
7 Meat-and-potato dish (9,3)
8 Incentive (4)
13 Perplexed (7)
15 OT prophet (7)
17 Not the clergy (5)
18 Greek hero (4)
20 Land owned by parish (5)

101

Across

1 Velocity (5)
4 Parade (5)
8 Insect (3)
9 Throttle (11)
10 Influence (7)
12 Vision (5)
13 Substitute (6)
14 Alter (6)
17 Anaesthetic (5)
19 Move on (7)
21 Deducting (11)
23 Add (3)
24 Glacial ridge (5)
25 Herb (5)

Down

1 Bantu language (5)
2 And so on (3)
3 Thinning agent (7)
4 Gloomy (6)
5 Trade (anag.) (5)
6 Northern duck (9)
7 Bid (7)
11 Speedily (9)
13 Carry into effect (7)
15 Pigeon roost (7)
16 More just (6)
18 Inventor of a famous cube (5)
20 Aglee (anag.) (5)
22 Climbing plant (3)

Across
1 Tar; AB (6)
4 Herr Ober (German) (6)
9 Lebanese tree (5)
10 Twizzled (7)
11 Anger (3)
12 Regulations (5)
13 Egg pasta; simpletons (7)
15 Blest delays (anag.) (4-2,5)
19 Tenth month (7)
20 Stolen goods dealer (5)
21 Winning serve; hole in one (3)
22 Kilt pouch (7)
24 Florida beach (5)
25 Island off mainland China (6)
26 Twist in agony (6)

Down
1 Safe (6)
2 Compliant (9)
3 Perfume root (5)
5 Grand Canyon state (7)
6 – Farlow, jazz guitarist (3)
7 Most vulgar (6)
8 £20,000 (slang) (6,5)
14 Lurk (3,2,4)
16 Monrovia's country (7)
17 Hardy country (6)
18 La Serenissima (6)
20 Thigh-bone (5)
23 Kimono sash (3)

103

Across

1 Knot (3)
3 Boring (4)
5 Coiffure (4)
8 Outrage (8)
10 Composition (4)
11 Hundred (3)
13 Study (5)
14 Apposite (9)
16 Before (3)
17 Lapse (3)
19 Loathsome (9)
21 Tally (5)
22 Stitch (3)
24 Sack (4)
25 Middling (8)
26 Ultimate (4)
27 Astound (4)
28 Dram (3)

Down

1 Flog (4)
2 Threadbare (4)
3 Behead (10)
4 Tiny (6)
6 Clapping (8)
7 Sonorous (8)
9 Spire (5)
12 Change (10)
14 Tranquil (8)
15 Needs (8)
18 Conclude (5)
20 Frank (6)
22 Survey (4)
23 Bawl (4)

Across

1 Carries (5)
4 Shoe bottoms (5)
10 Guarded (7)
11 Where butter's made (5)
12 Tier (5)
13 Sea trip (anag.) (7)
15 Scoffs (4)
17 Pretended (5)
19 Requires (5)
22 Statistics (4)
25 Range of pitch (7)
27 Hold (5)
29 Dealer (5)
30 More filthy (7)
31 Unit of length (5)
32 Sorts (5)

Down

2 Premature (5)
3 Umpire (7)
5 Rank (5)
6 Lived (7)
7 Climb (5)
8 Dozed (5)
9 Romany (5)
14 Tins (anag.) (4)
16 Tots (4)
18 Vie (7)
20 In a keen manner (7)
21 Expanse of water (5)
23 Privately (5)
24 Musical drama (5)
26 Following (5)
28 Animated (5)

105

Across

1 Scare (6)
5 Rule (5)
9 Innumerable (9)
10 Aficionado (3)
11 Be in debt (3)
12 Modern language (9)
14 Mate (3)
16 A vicious growl (5)
18 Tropical vegetable (3)
19 Inventive (9)
21 Perform (3)
22 Heart (3)
23 Television serial (4,5)
25 Live (5)
26 Snare (6)

Down

2 Become active (5)
3 Infers (7)
4 Digit (3)
5 Vertical part of stair (5)
6 Early childhood (7)
7 Guarded in speech (3-9)
8 Highly skilled (12)
13 Keyboard instrument (5)
15 Can be read (7)
17 Get overlooked (4,3)
20 Of the nose (5)
21 Scene of action (5)
24 Beer (3)

Across

1 Clown (6)
4 Importance (6)
7 Dish with lamb (8)
9 Liqueur (7)
12 Country in Middle East (5)
13 Lacking flavour (5)
15 Song of yesteryear (5)
16 Asian river (5)
17 Pronouncements (5)
18 Heavy drinker (5)
19 Oval (7)
23 Not talkative (8)
24 Academic chap? (6)
25 Alcove (6)

Down

1 Irish writer (5,5)
2 Fair transaction (6,4)
3 In bondage (8)
4 Land in OT (4)
5 Travellers in NT (4)
6 Subsequent (4)
8 Former name of Cambodia (9)
10 Author's pseudonym (3,2,5)
11 Tendons (10)
14 Verbal attack (8)
20 Zeal (anag.) (4)
21 False god (4)
22 Agitation (4)

107

Across

1 Prison room (4)
3 Wait (4)
9 VIII (5)
10 Ethical speaker (9)
11 Forefinger (5)
12 Military group (4,5)
15 Squeeze (6)
17 Of a sloping type (6)
19 Place side by side (9)
21 Snapshot (5)
23 One studying flying saucers (9)
24 Shaver (5)
25 Naked (4)
26 Intense (4)

Down

1 Unconscious (8)
2 Delphinium (8)
4 Guarantee (6)
5 Most ghostly (7)
6 Elderly (4)
7 River of Hades (4)
8 Musical symbol (4)
13 Element, symbol F (8)
14 Stoppered bottle (8)
16 Temporary stay (7)
18 English city (6)
20 Admit (4)
21 Swine's flesh (4)
22 Percolate (4)

108

Across
1 Unmanly man (5)
4 Ado (4)
7 Small mountain (4)
8 Ascending (8)
9 Scandalous news item (9)
10 Hole-boring tool (3)
12 Atomic nucleus;
   is more (anag.) (6)
14 Severe trial (6)
16 Tree (3)
18 Fourth day of the week (9)
21 Huge 17s (8)
22 Website (1-3)
23 Greek god (4)
24 Seats (anag.) (5)

Down
1 Black eyes (slang) (7)
2 Identical (8)
3 Sailing vessel (5)
4 White lies (4)
5 Tendon (5)
6 Japanese robe (6)
11 Homer's wandering hero (8)
13 Joint; spliff (6)
15 Unyielding (7)
17 Piece of rock (5)
19 Vanessa (abbrev.) (5)
20 Sad to say! (4)

109

Across

1 Upland (4)
3 Italian painter (6)
9 Planet (7)
10 Cheat (5)
11 Fish eggs (3)
12 Actor (9)
13 Cuban leader (6)
14 Short stout stick (6)
16 Mugger (9)
19 Unwell (3)
21 Path (5)
22 Backer (7)
23 Conundrum (6)
24 Stringed instrument (4)

Down

1 Large country house (5)
2 Legendary musician (7)
4 Foreword (12)
5 Expression (5)
6 Organic (7)
7 A rye bread (12)
8 Expensive (4)
13 Mat (7)
15 Lincs port (7)
17 Tolerate (5)
18 In addition (4)
20 Big (5)

Across
1 Troglodytes (4)
3 Metal thread (4)
9 Relative (5)
10 Started (9)
11 Slowly (mus.) (5)
12 Ability to be fair (9)
15 Christian festival (6)
17 Chronic breathing condition (6)
19 Study of religious art (9)
21 Intertwine (5)
23 Respiratory disease (9)
24 Foreign (5)
25 Story (4)
26 Not new (4)

Down
1 Pipes with finger holes (8)
2 Most wicked (8)
4 Purpose (6)
5 Everlasting (7)
6 Cathedral dignitary (4)
7 Nothing (4)
8 Jetty (4)
13 Demonstrable principles (8)
14 US state (8)
16 Obvious (7)
18 Force (6)
20 Marble-like gemstone (4)
21 Pound (4)
22 Mine opening (4)

The Telegraph

111

Across

1 Amorous liaison (6)
4 Sell (6)
7 Outlook (8)
9 Answered (7)
12 Mistake (5)
13 Legal ownership (5)
15 Contentious point (5)
16 North European (5)
17 Former gold coin (5)
18 Narcotic (5)
19 Continual (7)
23 Aspiration (8)
24 Deferred payment (6)
25 Spiritual beings (6)

Down

1 Grow in value (10)
2 Brandished (10)
3 Brought in from abroad (8)
4 Charge per unit (4)
5 Labour (4)
6 Do nothing (4)
8 Disapproval expressed (9)
10 Vague (10)
11 Decides (10)
14 Native of Tallinn (8)
20 Close (4)
21 Burden (4)
22 Sodium chloride (4)

The Telegraph

Across

1 Yield (4)
4 Root crop (6)
7 Born (3)
9 Fair (4)
10 Tedious (8)
11 Adam's partner (3)
12 Stove (4)
13 It's now Zimbabwe (8)
16 Reinsert screw (anag.) (13)
19 Most rigid (8)
23 Cover over (4)
24 Mischievous fairy (3)
25 Embarkation (8)
26 Very small (4)
27 Garden implement (3)
28 Group of seven (6)
29 Act (4)

Down

2 A beating about the bush (12)
3 International understanding (7)
4 Rock-like apostle (5)
5 Trunk of body (5)
6 Discernment (5)
8 Being everywhere at once (12)
14 Wails (5)
15 Welshman's name (3)
17 Mischievous fairy! (3)
18 Lured (7)
20 Spiny shrub (5)
21 Have being (5)
22 Drunk (5)

113

Across

1 In what way? (3)
3 Teeming (8)
9 Festivity (5)
10 Prohibited by law (7)
11 Duty (3)
13 One who fears foreigners (9)
14 Milky Way (6)
16 Truth (6)
18 First check;
   slate path (anag.) (5,4)
20 – whiz! (3)
22 Articles from abroad (7)
23 Three-masted vessel (5)
25 Give active force (8)
26 Chum (3)

Down

1 Go away! (3,2)
2 Period of hostilities (3)
4 Neigh (6)
5 Repeals (anag.) (7)
6 Developing inwards (9)
7 Covered walk (7)
8 Bobcat (4)
12 Percussion instrument (9)
14 Seductive look (4,3)
15 Photographing (1-6)
17 French motor-race
   venue (2,4)
19 Bible passage (4)
21 Outshine (5)
24 Bread roll (3)

114

Across

1 – Dresdel (actress) or Rykiel (designer) (5)
4 Ill-humour (6)
9 Hirsute (5)
10 Misfortune; relapse (7)
11 Charlotte Bronte novel (7)
12 e.g. Quavers (5)
14 Not in (3)
15 Self (3)
16 Last month (abbrev.) (3)
18 Equality (3)
21 Part of a shoe (5)
22 French enamel town (7)
23 Reddish purple (7)
25 US President (5)
26 Sting-ray (6)
27 Sunk fences (2-3)

Down

1 Breach in church unity (6)
2 Fixing to a wall (7,2)
3 – – Iron (song) (3,3)
5 Compass; scope (6)
6 Top golfers' body (abbrev.) (3)
7 Dissolute (6)
8 Be sensible! (slang) (3,4,4)
13 Great help (anag.) (9)
17 Peak (6)
18 Quickly; immediately (slang) (6)
19 Evenly spread (6)
20 Tries; attempts (6)
24 Tent rope (3)

115

Across

1 Hock (4)
3 Mortal (5)
7 Component (4)
8 Impromptu (10)
9 Jamboree (4)
12 Worsened (11)
13 Swelter (5)
15 Broom (5)
19 Unsurpassed (11)
21 Thug (4)
23 Carpenter (10)
24 Adhesive (4)
25 Prevent (5)
26 Secular (4)

Down

1 Pillaging (10)
2 Centre (7)
3 Greeted (6)
4 Reciprocal (6)
5 Elbow (5)
6 Lass (4)
10 Totals (4)
11 Lopsided (10)
14 Moreover (4)
16 Bewitch (7)
17 Religious (6)
18 Glare (6)
20 Single (5)
22 Smarmy (4)

Across
1 Male elephant (4)
3 Ladies' underwear (8)
9 Children's comic (5)
10 In pole position (7)
11 Affirmative! (3)
13 Australian animal (5,4)
14 High-voiced male singer (6)
16 Spin at speed (6)
18 Carrion-feeder (9)
20 Pinch (3)
22 Foreign objects collectively (7)
23 Full of gossip (5)
25 Nocturnal bird of swift family (8)
26 First class! (1-3)

Down
1 (Local) policeman (5)
2 Meadow (3)
4 I agree wholeheartedly! (3,3)
5 Corn storehouse (7)
6 Explode in anger (5,4)
7 Fencing warning (2,5)
8 Boat mooring (4)
12 Form of audience participation (9)
14 Famous sculptor (7)
15 Drugstore (7)
17 Tropical tree-lizard (6)
19 Ladder step (4)
21 To whom cheque is written (5)
24 Which person? (3)

117

Across

1 A heavy dull sound (4)
4 Rely (on) (6)
7 A metal-bearing mineral (3)
9 Rotate (4)
10 Offshoots (8)
11 Equipment (3)
12 Wander (4)
13 Lookouts (8)
16 Thoughtfulness (13)
19 People under the doctor (8)
23 Military force (4)
24 Section of circle (3)
25 Interrogate (8)
26 Suspend (4)
27 Perish (3)
28 Niche (6)
29 Corrode (4)

Down

2 Large thick-skinned herbivore (12)
3 Beasts of burden (7)
4 Financial obligations (5)
5 Obvious (5)
6 More pleasant (5)
8 Advances in a process (12)
14 Occurrence (5)
15 Hot drink (3)
17 Form of water (3)
18 Instructor (7)
20 Subject of debate (5)
21 Racket (5)
22 Rubs smooth (5)

Across

4 Shouted (6)
5 Become weary (4)
7 Makes (7)
10 Group of soldiers (5)
11 City in Pakistan (7)
12 Matter for discussion (5)
14 Versus (7)
15 Subdue (5)
16 Homes for dogs (7)
20 Supplicate (5)
21 Senator (anag.) (7)
22 Fool (4)
23 Unresponsive person (6)

Down

1 Change slightly (5)
2 High body temperature (5)
3 Someone like Pepys (7)
4 Inter (4)
6 Second book of OT (6)
8 In a knotty mess (7)
9 Important (7)
10 Scotland's emblem (7)
13 Hairstyle; fish (6)
14 They turn litmus paper blue (7)
17 Mistake (5)
18 Dance music (5)
19 Jest (4)

119

Across

1 Contests (5)
5 Determined (3,2)
8 Contest (5)
9 Board (5)
10 Satirised (9)
11 Greek H (3)
12 Inkiest hype (anag.) (3,2,3,3)
15 The 'Rams' (5,6)
19 OT priest (3)
20 Sway (9)
22 Indian monetary unit (5)
23 Hostility (5)
24 Illuminated (3,2)
25 Lowest point (5)

Down

1 Picked up (8)
2 Old-fashioned woman's hat (3,3)
3 Industrial plant (8)
4 Pollen-bearing organ (6)
5 Scare away (4)
6 Ball-game (6)
7 Irritating person (slang) (4)
13 Dependant (6-2)
14 Cartoon character (4,4)
16 Light bat (6)
17 Citrus fruit (6)
18 Cried out sharply (6)
20 Small bottle (4)
21 Jump (4)

Across

- **4** Very short period (2,4)
- **7** City in southern France (8)
- **8** Maker (6)
- **10** Circus swing (7)
- **11** Responsibility (4)
- **13** Sticking (8)
- **14** Support (4)
- **16** Itch (4)
- **18** Accomplished (8)
- **19** Pagan symbol (4)
- **21** Level with (7)
- **22** Glutted (6)
- **24** Extortion (8)
- **25** Kit can (anag.) (6)

Down

- **1** Driver of stolen vehicle (8)
- **2** Beaten with indoor shoe (9)
- **3** Questioning (9)
- **4** Novel (3)
- **5** Gets in (anag.) (6)
- **6** Existence (6)
- **9** Flow (3)
- **11** At right-angles to ship's course (2,3,4)
- **12** Female theatre attendant (9)
- **15** Disgust (8)
- **16** Making one (6)
- **17** Boring tool (6)
- **20** Be in debt (3)
- **23** Study (3)

The Telegraph

121

Across

1 Remain (4)
5 Male animal (4)
7 Lift (7)
8 News broadcast (8)
10 Troublesome person (4)
12 Daintily pleasing (4)
14 Memento (8)
16 State of nervous uncertainty (8)
17 Test (4)
18 Pile for burning corpse (4)
19 Undiluted (8)
22 It injects or extracts fluids (7)
23 Protest (4)
24 Exploit (4)

Down

1 Attempt (4)
2 Bawl (4)
3 Reject (8)
4 Profit (4)
5 Italian cheese (3,5)
6 Cheerful song (4)
9 South American country (7)
11 Vegetable (7)
13 Coffee (8)
15 Infallible (8)
18 Small lake (4)
19 A European national (4)
20 Piece of information (4)
21 Protruding tooth (4)

Across

1 Tall grasses (5)
4 Dug out (5)
10 Talk in a low voice (7)
11 Picture (5)
12 Facial features (5)
13 Student (7)
15 Enthusiastic about (4)
17 Venom (5)
19 Father (5)
22 Long periods (4)
25 Majestic quality (7)
27 Prime number (5)
29 Workers' federation (5)
30 Easier (7)
31 Words spoken in an undertone (5)
32 Totalled (5)

Down

2 Goes out (5)
3 Put down (7)
5 A nationality (5)
6 Permitted (7)
7 Golfer's movement (5)
8 Fidelity (5)
9 Tired (5)
14 Cipher (4)
16 Trim (4)
18 School subject (7)
20 Supposed (7)
21 Game fish (5)
23 Romany (5)
24 Irate (5)
26 Put in a row (5)
28 Worth (5)

123

Across

1 Overlooked (6)
5 Yearns (5)
9 Moving staircase (9)
10 Gamble (3)
11 Blade (3)
12 Greenhouses (9)
14 Total (3)
16 Senior (5)
18 Large body of salt water (3)
19 Wrong (9)
21 Headdress (3)
22 Employ (3)
23 Head of faculty (9)
25 Improve (5)
26 Rubbish (6)

Down

2 Bring upon oneself (5)
3 Quiet (7)
4 Point (3)
5 Concur (5)
6 Crossbreeds (7)
7 Acceptable (12)
8 Restructure (12)
13 Rooftop (5)
15 Jungle chopper (7)
17 Back out (7)
20 Lassoed (5)
21 Overly eager speed (5)
24 Night bird (3)

124

Across

1 Crescent-shaped space (7)
5 Small arachnids (5)
8 Obsequious person (5)
9 Rude (7)
10 In enchanting manner (9)
12 Regret (3)
13 Manipulate deviously (6)
14 Accompanying attendant (6)
17 Goon (3)
18 Good health! (7,2)
20 Fictitious excuse (7)
21 Spanish wine (5)
23 Tread (anag.) (5)
24 Sister of Orestes (7)

Down

1 Stand-in professional (5)
2 Born (female) (3)
3 Of current interest (7)
4 Peers (6)
5 Cheap and nasty (5)
6 Roomy (9)
7 Financially sound (7)
11 Bend the knee (9)
13 Big lie (7)
15 Whip (7)
16 Piece of sculpture (6)
18 Basic food (5)
19 Public square (5)
22 Not in fashion (3)

125

Across

1 Hindrance (8)
8 Rough (6)
9 Trinkets (6)
10 Make an appearance (4,1,3)
11 Shun (6)
13 Edentata (anag.) (8)
17 Old joke (8)
20 Hamper (6)
23 The − − is the better horse (4,4)
25 Slightly indecent (6)
26 Air travel (6)
27 Civil dignitaries (8)

Down

2 Highest happiness (5)
3 Cog (5)
4 Steersman (8)
5 Resound (4)
6 Risk (6)
7 Appearance (6)
11 Long poem (4)
12 Piece of soap (4)
14 Tied animals up (8)
15 Sour (4)
16 Always (4)
18 Barrier (6)
19 Thwart (6)
21 Prying person (5)
22 Escape adroitly (5)
24 Seaweed (4)

Across

1 Control strap (4)
4 Gravy vessel (4)
8 Big defeat (4)
9 Seemingly true (9)
11 Mission (6)
13 Till operator (7)
15 Boil (6)
16 Divided (6)
18 Punctual (2,4)
20 Savage (6)
22 Fearful (7)
23 Speaker (6)
25 Branches (9)
26 Somewhat (1,3)
27 Parasite (4)
28 Ringing sound (4)

Down

2 Slippery fishes (4)
3 Chewy sweet (6)
4 Joyful (6)
5 Snoozing (6)
6 Religious house (9)
7 Breeding horse (4)
10 Wayward (7)
12 European capital (4)
13 That's life! (4,2,3)
14 Wash scalp (7)
17 Action (4)
19 Rebuke (6)
20 Carnival (6)
21 Increase (3,3)
23 Uttered by mouth (4)
24 Knock out (4)

127

Across

1 Blue (5)
4 Falsity (3)
6 Equipment (3)
8 Morality (13)
9 Coliseum (5)
11 Simpleton (4)
13 Dishonour (5)
14 Bonkers (5)
15 Rustic (5)
16 Hades (4)
18 Observant (5)
21 Unemotional (13)
23 Sister (3)
24 Peak (3)
25 Plump (5)

Down

1 Scared (6)
2 Yearning (4)
3 Surplus (5)
4 Toilet (3)
5 Rapture (7)
6 Memento (8)
7 Brawl (6)
10 Ghostly (5)
12 Devotee (8)
14 Brazen (7)
15 Blush (6)
17 Solitary (6)
19 Squad (5)
20 Difficult (4)
22 Drink (3)

Across
1 Generated (4)
3 Wearied (5)
7 Small distance (4)
8 Peeress (10)
9 Departed (4)
12 Growth of troublesome animals (11)
13 Light-purple (5)
15 Vision (5)
19 Extremely impressive (11)
21 Large plant (4)
23 Suitable (10)
24 Sporting occasion (4)
25 Notches (5)
26 Always (4)

Down
1 Charitable (10)
2 Predicament (7)
3 Bending (6)
4 Aloof (6)
5 Wild dog (5)
6 Religious painting (4)
10 At any time (4)
11 Counter (10)
14 Mislay (4)
16 Ordinary (7)
17 Relating to the stage (6)
18 Fondle (6)
20 Nut (5)
22 Raise (4)

129

Across

1 An ugly sight (7)
5 Wharf (4)
7 Swift (5)
8 Awards (6)
10 Coop (4)
11 Trousered (8)
13 Terminating (6)
14 Take out cover (6)
17 Crook (8)
19 Grime (4)
21 Pertaining to teeth (6)
22 Chorus (5)
23 Secondhand (4)
24 Entraps (anag.) (7)

Down

1 Economy in production (10)
2 Came out (7)
3 Imprecation (4)
4 Take on (staff) (6)
5 Speeds up (8)
6 Broker (5)
9 Dangerous undertakings (10)
12 Maintained (8)
15 Mythical beast (7)
16 Gait of a horse (6)
18 Concepts (5)
20 Cicatrice (4)

The Telegraph

130

Across
1 Adopt (4,2)
4 Deer (4)
9 Sorts (5)
10 Consume excessively (7)
11 Cheese (7)
12 W H –, poet (5)
13 Conflicts (6)
15 Black Sea port (6)
18 Gorge (5)
20 Set forth (7)
23 Indulgent (7)
24 Earthenware (5)
25 Musical instrument (4)
26 Person in charge (6)

Down
1 NT book (5)
2 Rudyard –, author (7)
3 Disturbed (5)
5 Lover of Héloïse (7)
6 Border river (5)
7 Hip maybe (5)
8 Unit of poem (6)
13 Simplistic (6)
14 Shakespearean storm? (7)
16 Seedy (7)
17 Small-minded (5)
19 Cancel (5)
21 Drape (anag.) (5)
22 Put off (5)

131

Across

1 Indian language (5)
4 – Boleyn (4)
8 Loan (3)
9 Landmass (9)
10 Baghdad's country (4)
11 – Amadeus Mozart (8)
12 Covered wagon (3)
13 Moved sideways (6)
14 Former pupil (3,3)
16 Chopper (3)
17 Injured person (8)
18 Family (4)
20 Meat-eater (9)
21 Songbird (3)
22 In the past (4)
23 To the point (5)

Down

1 Mock title (3,4)
2 Part of the Sahara (6,6)
3 Peruvian Indian (4)
4 Innermost membrane (6)
5 Final lie (anag.) (4-4)
6 Baby carriage (12)
7 Male deer (4)
11 Bundle (3)
12 Innovate (anag.);
a system of blood vessels (8)
14 Acid (prefix) (3)
15 Chinese river (7)
16 In (2,4)
17 Rooster (4)
19 Joke (4)

132

Across

1 Stove (6)
7 Town with a charter (7)
8 Apparent shift in position of a star (8)
9 Eyed greedily (5)
10 Not abridged (5)
11 Plunge (4)
12 Pile up (5)
15 Aluminium alloy (5)
16 Father (5)
19 True (4)
20 No longer asleep (5)
21 Artsy (anag.) (5)
22 & 23 Kookaburra (8,7)
24 Rapidly changed focus (6)

Down

1 Caught (8)
2 Publicly known (2,6)
3 Israeli port (5)
4 Reynard (3)
5 Fairground car (6)
6 Exit (6)
7 Bullfighters' darts (11)
9 Egg-shaped (4)
13 Fish-tank (8)
14 Serrated (3-5)
15 Ryde (anag.) (4)
17 OT mount (6)
18 Rid sky (anag.); winter sport kit (3,3)
20 – -Saxon (5)
22 Old money (abbrev.) (3)

133

Across

1 Tree (5)
4 Loud shout (4)
8 Rum (7)
9 Piercing (5)
10 Outdo (5)
11 Plant (7)
13 On an aircraft (6)
15 Stretch of time (6)
17 Amazing (7)
20 Irritate (5)
22 Mediterranean fruit (5)
23 Friendly (7)
24 Body of followers (4)
25 Make alterations in (5)

Down

1 It contains scriptures (5)
2 Book of knowledge (12)
3 Athlete (7)
4 Terse (5)
5 Combine into a whole (5)
6 Suspect (12)
7 Messenger (6)
12 Type of music (3)
13 River (6)
14 Barrier (3)
16 Avoiding the issue (7)
18 Fat (5)
19 Praise (5)
21 Submit (5)

Across

1 The end (5)
3 Flung (6)
7 Pastry confection (5,4)
9 Heavy footwear (4)
10 Follow (a suspect) (4)
11 Dried corn stalks (5)
13 Igloo-dweller (6)
14 Winning bronze (5)
15 Verify (5)
17 How things are (2,2,2)
20 Telephone box (5)
21 Sudden misfortune (4)
23 A defect (4)
24 Two-step (mus.) (4,5)
25 Quash (6)
26 Deadly sin (5)

Down

1 Two times (6)
2 Legal wrong (4)
3 Upper-class (3-3)
4 Floating log structure (4)
5 Of high birth (5)
6 Division of poem (5)
7 Over the moon (4-1-4)
8 'Once upon a time...' (5,4)
11 Slap (5)
12 Kitchen utensil (5)
16 Nonsense (6)
17 Royal racecourse (5)
18 Hero of US literature (6)
19 The depths (5)
22 Unit of electricity (4)
23 Open tart (4)

135

Across

1 Sweet juicy gourd (5)
4 Sheepdog (6)
7 Able to see (7)
8 Nuzzle (4)
10 Complete (5)
11 Portable lamp (7)
14 A long time (4)
16 Marine reptile (6)
18 Guardian (6)
21 Chuck (4)
23 Serious (7)
26 Pursue (5)
27 Just (4)
28 Revealed (7)
29 Begins (6)
30 Unfortunately (5)

Down

1 Bearers of malaria (10)
2 Supply boat (7)
3 Innate (7)
4 Embrace (6)
5 Fabric from flax (5)
6 Point for discussion (5)
9 Hostile (10)
12 Requests (4)
13 Draw (3)
15 Obtains (4)
17 Prepare leather (3)
19 Gets away (7)
20 Lauded (7)
22 Freshwater mammals (6)
24 Respond (5)
25 Mistake (5)

Across

1 Magic rod? (4)
4 Inaccuracy (5)
8 Edible fish (4,4)
9 Leave (4)
10 Continuous change (4)
11 Collected (8)
12 Item of neckwear (6)
14 Shrewd (6)
16 Uniter of Germany (8)
19 Close to (4)
20 Hitlerite (4)
21 Two-way conversation (8)
22 Very fat (5)
23 Profound (4)

Down

2 Append (5)
3 Lack of rain (7)
4 Cairo's country (5)
5 Petition (7)
6 European river (5)
7 Cricketer; hat (6)
13 Bloodsucking creature (7)
14 Clumsy (7)
15 Drinking vessel (6)
17 American state (5)
18 Raised edge (5)
19 Hangman's knot (5)

137

Across

1 IV in Roman numerals (4)
3 Vision (5)
7 Long story (4)
8 South American rodent (10)
9 South American ostrich (4)
12 Fleshy part of bird's tail (7,4)
13 Flimsy (5)
15 Drink (colloq.) (5)
19 Pilot's emergency device (7-4)
21 Demolish (4)
23 Jockey (10)
24 Seaweed (4)
25 Cleft (5)
26 Instead (4)

Down

1 Make-up (4-6)
2 Calls (5,2)
3 Egyptian statue (6)
4 Lead sulphide (6)
5 Russian emperors (5)
6 Leer (4)
10 Conqueror (4)
11 Approval (10)
14 Egyptian port (4)
16 Obverse (anag.) (7)
17 Real (6)
18 Fondle (6)
20 Military vehicles (5)
22 So be it (4)

138

Across

1 Quintet (4)
4 Poet (4)
8 Manner of walking (4)
9 Facing difficulty (2,7)
11 Catch (6)
13 Osculating (7)
15 Language (6)
16 Bathroom powder (6)
18 Stumps (6)
20 Make dispirited (6)
22 Settled (7)
23 Hill near Telford (6)
25 Admission gate (9)
26 Heavy hammer (4)
27 Listen (4)
28 Portal (4)

Down

2 Hebridean island (4)
3 Insect with pincers (6)
4 Rubles (anag.) (6)
5 Soften (6)
6 Jeered (9)
7 Prevent (4)
10 In use (7)
12 Casserole (4)
13 Constructed hastily (7,2)
14 Copyread (7)
17 Fable (4)
19 Neuter (anag.) (6)
20 Repast (6)
21 Joked (6)
23 Feeble person (4)
24 Male voice (4)

139

Across

1 Set of furniture (5)
4 Moan (5)
10 Native American dwellings (7)
11 Chuckle (5)
12 Ridge (5)
13 Central European republic (7)
15 Beams of light (4)
17 Money (slang) (5)
19 Large bird of prey (5)
22 Peck (4)
25 Own (7)
27 More secure (5)
29 Foe (5)
30 Opens out (7)
31 A test (anag.) (5)
32 Totalled (5)

Down

2 Pressed (5)
3 Sellers (7)
5 Entrance passages (5)
6 Taking no sides (7)
7 Rise into waves (5)
8 Attempt (5)
9 Bread ingredient (5)
14 Employs (4)
16 Requests (4)
18 Consideration (7)
20 Confident (7)
21 Pace (5)
23 Offspring (5)
24 Push (5)
26 North African republic (5)
28 Wrong (5)

Across

1 Ruff (6)
4 Prosperous (4)
8 Batter (6)
9 Respect (6)
10 Hilarity (5)
11 Obstruction (7)
13 Trim (4)
15 Nothing (3)
16 Swag (4)
18 Broken (7)
20 Consecrate (5)
23 Throughout (6)
24 Beginning (6)
25 Low (4)
26 Pinch (6)

Down

1 Warning (7)
2 Constraint (5)
3 Associate (4)
5 Sinful (7)
6 Swarm (5)
7 Competent (7)
12 Withstand (7)
14 Hobby (7)
17 Lewd (7)
19 Knoll (5)
21 Limber (5)
22 Humbug (4)

141

Across

1 Congregated (6)
4 Per person (6)
7 Performance areas (8)
9 Woods (7)
12 Frequently (5)
13 Wander (5)
15 Metric volume (5)
16 Notes (anag.) (5)
17 Impel (5)
18 Innocent (5)
19 Period of activity (7)
23 Posture (8)
24 Increase (6)
25 Climb (6)

Down

1 Static (10)
2 Viewers (10)
3 Stretched (8)
4 In addition to (4)
5 Lazy (4)
6 Actors in a play (4)
8 Functioning effectively (9)
10 Stand-in (10)
11 Small colony (10)
14 Lions eat (anag.) (8)
20 Middle Eastern ruler (4)
21 Goulash (4)
22 Curse (4)

142

Across

1 Dispatched (4)
3 For each one (6)
9 Examine (7)
10 Excuse in court (5)
11 Make a mistake (3)
12 Gift to an institution (9)
13 Expunge (6)
14 Wire fastener (6)
16 Canadian emblem (5,4)
19 Chafe (3)
21 Cake decoration (5)
22 Big tent (7)
23 Military greeting (6)
24 Barrier against water (4)

Down

1 Grab (5)
2 Nasal opening (7)
4 Take dangerous risks (4,4,4)
5 Banished person (5)
6 Letter in Bible (7)
7 Old gramophone record (7-5)
8 Male horse for breeding (4)
13 Realms (7)
15 Offence of lying under oath (7)
17 Small bottle (5)
18 Austen novel (4)
20 Long musical note (5)

143

Across

1 Bladed pole (3)
3 Row (3)
5 Hirsute (5)
8 Allocate (5)
9 US Congress building (7)
10 Hard work (4)
11 Of shepherds (8)
13 Leap in the air (4,2)
14 Big ace (anag.); cool carrier (3-3)
17 Carbon −; gas (8)
19 Russian emperor (4)
22 − − fertilisation (IVF) (2,5)
23 Derision (5)
24 Of gold (5)
25 Firmament (3)
26 Hardly any (3)

Down

1 Attack (5)
2 Mailers (anag.) (7)
3 Stag (4)
4 Drink of the gods (6)
5 Liverwort (8)
6 Bury (5)
7 Christmas fuel (4-3)
12 Chivalrous (8)
13 West Indian island (7)
15 Go away (4,3)
16 Abominable (6)
18 Not at all (5)
20 Regenerate (5)
21 Greyish (4)

Across

1 Feed with fuel (5)
5 1974 song by Barry Manilow (5)
8 Slang suffix denoting a place (5)
9 Russian edict (5)
10 Nanny (9)
11 Golf starting point (3)
12 Gibberish (6,5)
15 Brilliant (11)
19 Salesman (3)
20 Common weed (9)
22 Computer data (5)
23 Gaseous element (5)
24 Expel (5)
25 Wooded glen (5)

Down

1 Quartets (anag.) (8)
2 Approved (6)
3 Net value (anag.) (8)
4 Flowery (6)
5 Measure (4)
6 Swimming (6)
7 Enclosed area (4)
13 Residence (8)
14 Sanatorium (8)
16 Nap (6)
17 Prying (6)
18 Cup (6)
20 Strong wind (4)
21 Closest (4)

145

Across

1 Aromatic gum (5)
4 Discoverer of radium (5)
8 Tiny amount of money (3)
9 Art of sewing (11)
10 Herb (7)
12 Index (5)
13 Obstruct (6)
14 Interweave strands (6)
17 French capital (5)
19 Booze (7)
21 Chemical smelling of mothballs (11)
23 Perched (3)
24 Speak (5)
25 Evade (5)

Down

1 Exotic fruit (5)
2 Regret (3)
3 The Netherlands (7)
4 Silken sheath (6)
5 Respond (5)
6 Settle (9)
7 Harsh (7)
11 International language (9)
13 Whim (7)
15 Diving duck (7)
16 Fluster (6)
18 Cuttlefish ink (5)
20 Loyal vassal (5)
22 Close (3)

Across

1 Fasten (4)
4 Estimate (5)
8 Garden plant (5,3)
9 Irritable (4)
10 Interweave (4)
11 Final appearance (8)
12 Middle (6)
14 Song (6)
16 Collaborator (8)
19 Imitate (4)
20 Asian language (4)
21 Door (8)
22 Magnificent (5)
23 Three feet (4)

Down

2 Public (5)
3 Witty comeback (7)
4 African country (5)
5 Implement (7)
6 Scottish town (5)
7 Pinch (6)
13 Bear witness (7)
14 Intolerance (7)
15 Feature (6)
17 Escort (5)
18 Perfect (5)
19 Movable seat (5)

147

Across

1 Disguise (4)
3 Decoratively assembled (7)
8 Money earned (6)
9 Dale (6)
10 Appreciative (8)
11 Enclose (4)
12 Warning signals (6)
15 Sailing vessels (6)
17 Resign (4)
19 Areas for fruit growing (8)
22 Adapt (6)
23 Large felines (6)
24 Enigma (7)
25 Contributes (4)

Down

1 Not of legal age (5)
2 Gun (slang) (7)
4 Merrymaking (7)
5 Permit (5)
6 Graceful (7)
7 Submerged ridge (4)
13 Washing (7)
14 Brusquer (7)
16 Altered (7)
18 Confidence (5)
20 Quote (4)
21 Challenges (5)

Across

1 Engendered (4)
4 Origin (6)
7 Groove (3)
9 Jazzy dance (4)
10 Not copied (8)
11 Stitch (3)
12 Troublesome plant (4)
13 Excessive sentimentality (8)
16 Stupefied (13)
19 New male student (8)
23 Mysterious objects in sky (4)
24 Container for ashes (3)
25 Appealing to the masses (8)
26 Little devils (4)
27 Add (3)
28 Obdurate (6)
29 Way out (4)

Down

2 Make a great commotion (5,3,4)
3 German city (7)
4 Packs (5)
5 Husband of Bathsheba (5)
6 High-quality porcelain (5)
8 Something done and unalterable (4,8)
14 About (Latin) (5)
15 Floor covering (3)
17 First note of scale (3)
18 Bring back together (7)
20 Crouch (5)
21 Cereal crop (5)
22 Crackers (5)

149

Across
1 Pleads (4)
4 Golfer's peg (3)
6 Learning (4)
8 Take on loan (6)
9 Aiding digestion (6)
10 Ta (5,3)
11 Camera lens (4)
12 Shrewd bargainer (7-6)
17 Eager (4)
19 Fish-tank (8)
22 Joyous (6)
23 Easy (6)
24 Distant (4)
25 Flop (3)
26 – Gallery (4)

Down
2 Era (5)
3 Injector (7)
4 Brownish-yellow (5)
5 Explain (7)
6 Administrative capital of Bolivia (2,3)
7 Root (7)
10 Pull (3)
13 Divert assets (4,3)
14 Be laden (anag.) (7)
15 Orange-coloured fruit (7)
16 Tup (3)
18 Airer (5)
20 Not given food (5)
21 Until (anag.) (5)

Across

1 Canal city (6)
4 The Pequod? (6)
7 Name (8)
9 Captain (7)
12 Uptight (5)
13 Property levy (5)
15 Beef undercut (5)
16 Pure (5)
17 Last letter (5)
18 Top tennis player (5)
19 Fundamental (7)
23 Cell study (8)
24 Forever (6)
25 Done! (6)

Down

1 Thackeray novel (6,4)
2 Neutral area (2-4-4)
3 Musical composition (8)
4 Period of time (4)
5 On the summit of (4)
6 Fencing sword (4)
8 Cause of sleeping sickness (6,3)
10 'Mirror' word, e.g. mum, Abba (10)
11 Transferred (troops) (10)
14 Musician's last work (4,4)
20 Cain's brother (4)
21 US state (4)
22 5th NT book (4)

Solutions 1–2

1

Across:
1 *Graze*
4 *Ella*
8 *Gee* (Gray's Elegy)
9 Spectator
10 Rank
11 Kentucky
12 Fir
13 Napkin
14 Odessa
16 Due
17 Margaret
18 Bred
20 Wonderful
21 Din
22 Stun
23 Crete

Down:
1 Gagarin
2 Awe-inspiring
3 Easy
4 Exeter
5 Latitude
6 Stocksbridge
7 Fray
11 Kin
12 Filament
14 Out
15 Andante
16 Deafen
17 Mows
19 Bloc

2

Across:
1 *Doh*
3 *Dec*
5 *Anise* (Dodecanese)
8 Greek
9 Islands
10 Tutu
11 Shortage
13 Zipped
14 Dioxin
17 Squabble
19 Brum
22 Frigate
23 Auxin
24 Lined
25 Ebb
26 Day

Down:
1 Digit
2 Heeltap
3 DUKW
4 Chichi
5 Allergic
6 Ionia
7 Eastern
12 Keyboard
13 Zestful
15 Xeroxed
16 Sleeve
18 Union
20 Mangy
21 Jamb

Solutions 3-4

3

Across:
1 Flow
3 Tiller (Flotilla)
9 Kindred
10 Topic
11 Rub
12 Absorbent
13 Ersatz
14 Sequel
16 Divergent
19 Ray
21 Adieu
22 Oxonian
23 Seethe
24 Ness

Down:
1 Fakir
2 Omnibus
4 Interjection
5 Lapse
6 Recital
7 Breakthrough
8 Odes
13 Endears
15 Ukraine
17 Voice
18 Eros
20 Yanks

4

Across:
1 *Dees*
4 *Pick*
8 *Abel* (Despicable)
9 Traumatic
11 Lovely
13 Frazzle
15 Amoeba
16 Iritis
18 Fillip
20 Remote
22 Dunedin
23 Sewage
25 Ebullient
26 Fine
27 Hoax
28 Gown

Down:
2 Ezra
3 Square
4 Piazza
5 Chilli
6 Objection
7 Clay
10 Coerced
12 Waif
13 Following
14 Abridge
17 Seek
19 Pueblo
20 Reflex
21 Mixing
23 Soft
24 Anew

Solutions 5–6

5

Across:
1 *Like*
4 *Hub*
6 *Bear*
8 *Wither*
9 *Saw red* (Like a bear with a sore head)
10 Stockade
11 Real
12 Rolling Stones
17 Plug
19 Symphony
22 Encore
23 Nelson
24 Loot
25 Toy
26 Ouse

Down:
2 Idiot
3 Ethical
4 Horsa
5 Buskers
6 Bower
7 Average
10 Sir
13 Orlando
14 No sweat
15 Othello
16 Spy
18 Ghost
20 Money
21 Nooks

6

Across:
1 Leigh
4 Weigh (Leeway)
8 Ice
9 Benedictine
10 Approve
12 Miami
13 Strike
14 Acacia
17 Ivory
19 Halcyon
21 Memorabilia
23 Eye
24 Rhyme
25 Epoch

Down:
1 Libya
2 Inn
3 Haddock
4 Wicked
5 Idiom
6 Hierarchy
7 Replica
11 Performer
13 Spinney
15 Calibre
16 Charge
18 Yummy
20 Neath
22 Leo

Solutions 7-8

7

8

Solutions 9–10

9

Across:
1 Marshal
8 Hearts (Martial arts)
9 Squalid
11 Displace
12 Bison
14 Atom
15 Haricots
17 Imitator
18 Otto
20 Susan
21 Allergen
23 Diffuse
24 Litany
25 Textile

Down:
2 Acquit
3 Shalom
4 Avid
5 Leipzig
6 Breakouts
7 Aspersion
10 Disavowed
12 Basically
13 Socialite
16 Jarring
18 Outfit
19 Tassel
22 Nice

10

Across:
1 *Peter*
4 *Merits*
9 *Burgh* (Pietermaritzburg)
10 Matinee
11 Liaison
12 Impel
14 All
15 Ell
16 Ill
18 Ski
21 Canoe
22 Le Havre
23 Coal tit
25 South
26 Africa
27 Sited

Down:
1 Pebble
2 Tarpaulin
3 Rehash
5 Entail
6 Ion
7 Seemly
8 Amenability
13 Pole-vault
17 Acacia
18 Septic
19 Thesis
20 Method
24 Air

Solutions 11–12

11

Across:

1 *Wring out*
8 *Whiled*
9 *Belles* (Ring out wild bells)
10 Tentacle
11 Jenner
13 Espresso
17 Extremes
20 Income
23 Break out
25 Ignite
26 Severs
27 Tennyson

Down:

2 Reeve
3 Nylon
4 On-stream
5 Twin
6 Pirate
7 Welles
11 Jude
12 Neat
14 Position
15 So-so
16 Ogle
18 Xerxes
19 Reader
21 Canny
22 Motto
24 Oust

12

Across:

1 Connie
4 Furze (Conifers)
8 Acute
9 Radiant
10 Marital
11 Byre
12 Leg
14 Glut
15 Also
18 Yak
21 Chad
23 Inhabit
25 Torrent
26 Raise
27 Handy
28 Advert

Down:

1 Clammy
2 Neutral
3 Identity
4 Fade
5 Ready
6 Esteem
7 Grill
13 Gathered
16 Sublime
17 Scotch
19 Kitty
20 Street
22 Apron
24 Levy

The Telegraph

Solutions 13–14

13

Across:
4 Plaice
7 Settings (Place settings)
8 Ischia
10 Beloved
11 Real
13 Carefree
14 Less
16 Feta
18 True blue
19 Orgy
21 Causing
22 Mosque
24 Mal de mer
25 Landau

Down:
1 Renegade
2 Stroke oar
3 Integrity
4 Psi
5 Inhale
6 Exalts
9 See
11 Reputable
12 Alabaster
15 Squander
16 Formal
17 Tocsin
20 Gnu
23 Emu

14

Across:
1 *Seed*
3 *Heap*
9 *Layer* (CD player)
10 Crocodile
11 Annoy
12 Raindrops
15 Tuning
17 Admire
19 Musicians
21 Scrub
23 Elevation
24 Tower
25 Site
26 Used

Down:
1 Security
2 Emotions
4 Editor
5 Pleased
6 Hymn
7 Prey
8 Gold
13 Litanies
14 Reasoned
16 Numbers
18 Assent
20 Clap
21 Sits
22 Rows

Solutions 15-16

15

Across:
1 Purr
4 Swayed (Persuade)
7 Eel
9 Beef
10 Educator
11 Ire
12 Spin
13 Pleasure
16 Arc de Triomphe
19 Marquess
23 Jest
24 Too
25 Metaphor
26 Ream
27 Orc
28 De trop
29 Aver

Down:
2 Unexpurgated
3 Refined
4 Sleep
5 Azure
6 Exams
8 Fourth estate
14 Larks
15 Ago
17 Emu
18 Majorca
20 Quake
21 Ether
22 Strop

16

Across:
4 *Billed*
5 *Ding*
7 *Society* (Building society)
10 Divan
11 Trailer
12 Comma
14 Maudlin
15 Lovat
16 Tipster
20 Attic
21 Halifax
22 Wide
23 Nation

Down:
1 Plait
2 Delta
3 Pig-iron
4 Book
6 Gramme
8 Erratic
9 Yiddish
10 Decibel
13 Kowtow
14 Matilda
17 Tamar
18 Rigid
19 Dawn

Solutions 17–18

17

Across:
1 *Good*
3 *Mourning*
9 *Again*
10 *Mondays*
11 *Ear* (Good morning again, Monday's here!)
13 Walk Alone
14 Invade
16 Oscars
18 Waltz time
20 Ass
22 Ruinous
23 Three
25 Songfest
26 Four

Down:
1 Grave
2 Ova
4 Ormolu
5 Runways
6 Inamorata
7 Gospels
8 Anew
12 Revulsion
14 Inwards
15 Doze off
17 Kisses
19 Eats
21 Steer
24 Rio

18

Across:
1 *Blew*
3 *Wide*
9 *Buoys* (Blue-eyed boys)
10 Nightclub
11 Annoy
12 Interview
15 Heehaw
17 Cygnet
19 Top drawer
21 Solve
23 Menagerie
24 Cheap
25 Tutu
26 Spin

Down:
1 Bunfight
2 Eighteen
4 Inlaid
5 Ebb away
6 Gown
7 Espy
8 Stir
13 Snowdrop
14 Sturgeon
16 Attempt
18 Spinet
20 Rage
21 Sack
22 Leek

Solutions 19–20

19

Across:
7 Hissed
8 Oracle (Historical)
9 Steal a march on
10 Gossiped
12 Coda
13 Icon
15 Fortress
17 Martello tower
19 Saloon
20 Lean-to

Down:
1 Bistro
2 Assassination
3 Idea
4 Colander
5 Lance corporal
6 Almond
11 Piffling
14 Cravat
16 Siesta
18 Oslo

20

Across:
1 *Buys*
4 *Sick*
8 *Haul* (Bicycle)
9 Bilingual
11 Sudden
13 Postmen
15 Chorus
16 School
18 Source
20 Regret
22 Exposed
23 Planet
25 Decisions
26 Open
27 Adds
28 Says

Down:
2 Unit
3 Suitor
4 Sights
5 Chases
6 Cardboard
7 Plan
10 Lunches
12 Acts
13 Populated
14 Succeed
17 Late
19 Extend
20 Robins
21 Genius
23 Poor
24 Envy

Solutions 21–22

21

Across:
1 Ketchup
5 Later (Catch up later)
8 Filer
9 Quantum
10 Advance
11 Dwell
12 Jovial
14 Oyster
17 Niger
19 Recoups
22 Tuition
23 Exile
24 Refit
25 Yashmak

Down:
1 Kafka
2 Tel Aviv
3 Heron
4 Piquet
5 Leap day
6 Tithe
7 Rambler
12 Janitor
13 Airlift
15 Tourism
16 Frenzy
18 Grief
20 Chess
21 Sneak

22

Across:
1 *Para*
4 *Dice*
8 *Lost* (Paradise Lost)
9 Conscript
11 Eel-set
13 Unhitch
15 Milton
16 Keynes
18 Thirst
20 Salute
22 Tetanus
23 Shaver
25 Red salmon
26 Flue
27 John
28 Duty

Down:
2 Avon
3 Absent
4 Darwin
5 Copeck
6 Poisonous
7 Stet
10 Teheran
12 Emit
13 Ultimatum
14 Holster
17 Shed
19 Teredo
20 Samson
21 Lulled
23 Safe
24 Poet

Solutions 23–24

23

Across:
1 *Lemming*
5 *Tons*
7 *Paris*
8 *Really*
10 *Dull*
11 *Knightly* (Leamington Spa is really dull nightly)
13 Rescue
14 On time
17 Scotsman
19 Star
21 Handel
22 Limit
23 Lair
24 Dresser

Down:
1 Lapidarist
2 Marbles
3 Ipso
4 Goring
5 Twanging
6 Nilot
9 Typewriter
12 Outsider
15 Isthmus
16 Pallid
18 Obama
20 Clue

24

Across:
1 Cheque
5 Liszt (Checklist)
9 Philander
10 Ask
11 Coy
12 Roquefort
14 Asp
16 Least
18 Due
19 Decathlon
21 Lot
22 Pea
23 Badminton
25 Nadir
26 Danger

Down:
2 Hairy
3 Quarrel
4 End
5 Large
6 Seafood
7 Take the stand
8 Spick-and-span
13 Quail
15 Pochard
17 Tension
20 Tiber
21 Lithe
24 Dud

The Telegraph

Solutions 25–26

25

Across:
1 Waugh
4 Fair (Warfare)
8 Tad
9 Phenomena
10 Earl
11 Accurate
12 Tie
13 Saucer
14 Ailing
16 Ass
17 Foredeck
18 Bier
20 Financier
21 Awl
22 Lyre
23 Pieta

Down:
1 Witness
2 Undercurrent
3 Hype
4 Fleece
5 Iroquois
6 Rehabilitate
7 Mate
11 Air
12 Tendency
14 Ask
15 Gorilla
16 Active
17 Fife
19 Trip

26

Across:
1 *High*
4 *Iraq*
8 *Quay* (Hierarchy)
9 Delicious
11 Strike
13 Shelter
15 Rattle
16 Divide
18 Attics
20 Bearer
22 Thirsty
23 Summer
25 Dinosaurs
26 Inns
27 Mess
28 Kiln

Down:
2 Idea
3 Height
4 Icicle
5 Amused
6 Auxiliary
7 Type
10 Stripes
12 Area
13 Statement
14 Elected
17 Errs
19 Shrine
20 Brooms
21 Attack
23 Slim
24 Oral

Solutions 27-28

27

Across:
1 Reap
3 Ealing (Repealing)
9 Lettuce
10 Cider
11 Cue
12 Pakistani
13 Zephyr
14 French
16 Misquotes
19 Vex
21 Equip
22 Gremlin
23 Inlays
24 Dawn

Down:
1 Relic
2 Antwerp
4 Ancestresses
5 Indra
6 Garnish
7 Humpty Dumpty
8 Jerk
13 Zambezi
15 Novella
17 Skull
18 Toga
20 Xenon

28

Across:
1 *Wens*
4 *Lee*
6 *Dale* (Wensleydale)
8 Cheese
9 Platan
10 Trapdoor
11 Feta
12 Level-crossing
17 Half
19 Explicit
22 Florid
23 Settee
24 Edam
25 Ray
26 Note

Down:
2 Ether
3 Steeple
4 Lie to
5 Esparto
6 Dwarf
7 Leant on
10 Tel
13 Enabled
14 Cheddar
15 Stilton
16 Gut
18 Forum
20 Pesky
21 Inept

Solutions 29–30

29

Across:
1 *Beaks*
4 *Spider*
9 *Becks*
10 *Loverly*
11 *In a mist* (Bix Beiderbecke's lovely 'In a Mist')
12 Newel
14 Mog
15 Amy
16 Old
18 Tic
21 Older
22 Hawkeye
23 Ninepin
25 Naive
26 Tender
27 Yield

Down:
1 Bobbin
2 Acclaimed
3 Saskia
5 Paving
6 Dur
7 Royals
8 Slot machine
13 Wolverine
17 Cornet
18 Triple
19 Twenty
20 Defend
24 Nan

30

Across:
1 More
3 Hammered (Mohammed)
9 Tense
10 Stroppy
11 Had
13 Servitude
14 Tetchy
16 Odious
18 Mortality
20 Sum
22 Evident
23 Label
25 Treasure
26 Free

Down:
1 Match
2 Run
4 Absurd
5 Married
6 Rapturous
7 Dryness
8 Begs
12 Determine
14 Tempest
15 Heavens
17 Litter
19 Yell
21 Melee
24 Bar

Solutions 31–32

The Telegraph

Solutions 33–34

33

Across:
7 Fasten
8 Hating (Fascinating)
9 Discretionary
10 Diligent
12 Iowa
13 Just
15 Avengers
17 Cinematograph
19 Sequel
20 Geezer

Down:
1 Tahiti
2 Stick-in-the-mud
3 Knee
4 Christie
5 Standing order
6 Andrew
11 Erasable
14 Unisex
16 Rapier
18 Orgy

34

Across:
1 Fore
3 Shack (Dvorak)
7 Neat
8 Resistance
9 Ever
12 Intolerable
13 Dated
15 Spree
19 Illusionist
21 Gale
23 Effervesce
24 Chic
25 Halve
26 Thus

Down:
1 Forbidding
2 Episode
3 Setter
4 Annual
5 Kneel
6 Wave
10 Veer
11 Relentless
14 Tail
16 Pungent
17 Rueful
18 Pierce
20 Leech
22 Ache

Solutions 35–36

35

Across:
1 *Port*
5 *Rate*
7 *Gallery* (Portrait gallery)
8 Spruce up
10 Gath
12 Mend
14 Wiseacre
16 Betrayal
17 Slam
18 Zeus
19 Pictured
22 Veranda
23 Tate
24 Huff

Down:
1 Puss
2 T G W U
3 Alleyway
4 Kelp
5 Rye-grass
6 Etch
9 Precede
11 Terrace
13 Derisive
15 Silicone
18 Zest
19 Perk
20 Utah
21 Daff

36

Across:
1 *Kind*
4 *Arson*
8 *Coronets* (Kind Hearts and Coronets)
9 Alec
10 Pity
11 Guinness
12 Island
14 Genome
16 Panorama
19 MMIX
20 Vine
21 Grumpier
22 Miser
23 Lady

Down:
2 Irony
3 Dredged
4 Assai
5 Shannon
6 Needs
7 Movies
13 Avocets
14 Gradual
15 Maiden
17 Axiom
18 Anger
19 Moped

The Telegraph

Solutions 37–38

37

Across:
1 Too
3 Fake (Toothache)
5 Bias
8 Pregnant
10 Limb
11 Oar
13 Naive
14 Diffident
16 Woe
17 Tug
19 Interfere
21 Larks
22 Map
24 Idea
25 Feminine
26 Gash
27 Cede
28 Eat

Down:
1 Typo
2 Over
3 Fanaticism
4 Kindle
6 Initiate
7 Submerge
9 Radio
12 Enterprise
14 Dwelling
15 Fearless
18 Urban
20 Thieve
22 Mine
23 Pert

38

Across:
7 Missed
8 Aching (Mistaking)
10 Lie-down
11 Accra
13 Tame
15 Stock
17 Blind
19 Deep
23 Jelly
25 Cheroot
26 Savour
27 Oeuvre

Down:
1 Amulet
2 Esteem
3 Heron
4 Scratch
5 Zinc
6 Agra
9 Knot
12 Ridge
14 Ankle
16 Playful
18 Neck
20 Evolve
21 Patter
22 Jewel
23 Just
24 Live

Solutions 39-40

39

Across:
1 Deign
4 Germany (Danger money)
8 Oar
9 Wants
10 Optical
11 Pleasantly
14 Update
16 Advise
18 Guaranteed
22 Example
23 Brain
24 Nil
25 Pleaded
26 Essay

Down:
1 Downpour
2 Innuendo
3 Noses
4 Ground
5 Rattled
6 Arch
7 Yell
12 Sideways
13 Tendency
15 Thumped
17 Friend
19 Noble
20 Help
21 Bare

40

Across:
1 Hare
3 Dressers (Hairdressers)
9 Mamba
10 Texture
11 Raj
13 Pineapple
14 Family
16 Stress
18 Nostalgia
20 Tin
22 Treason
23 Blaze
25 Canon law
26 Whey

Down:
1 Homer
2 Ram
4 Retina
5 Sextant
6 Equipment
7 Seekers
8 Vamp
12 James Dean
14 Fanatic
15 Liaison
17 Uganda
19 Ambo
21 Needy
24 Ash

Solutions 41-42

41

Across:
1 *Bloc*
4 *Kay*
6 *Did* (Blockaded)
9 Rex
10 Runic
11 Adept
12 Jack Sprat
15 Consequential
19 Vanishing
21 Multi
22 Offal
24 Tit
25 Kew
26 Six
27 Duck

Down:
2 Lexicon
3 Corps
4 Kin
5 Yucatan
6 Dozen
7 Drat
8 Project
13 Rouen
14 Flighty
16 Envious
17 Idiotic
18 Allow
20 Salad
21 Monk
23 Fax

42

Across:
1 *Vault*
4 *Airs*
8 *Candide* (Voltaire's Candide)
9 Paris
10 Latin
11 Andante
13 Accent
15 Orchid
17 Channel
20 Stoic
22 Pylon
23 On-drive
24 Byes
25 Dread

Down:
1 Vocal
2 Unnoticeable
3 Trianon
4 Arena
5 Rapid
6 French police
7 Ascend
12 NCO
13 Accept
14 The
16 Resided
18 Nancy
19 Lions
21 Creed

Solutions 43-44

43

Across:
1 Beer
3 Tricks (Beatrix)
9 Egghead
10 Orbit
11 Tie
12 Elaborate
13 Brolly
14 Pebble
16 Wolfhound
19 Rob
21 Trail
22 Apostle
23 Honest
24 Calm

Down:
1 Brest
2 El Greco
4 Rhododendron
5 Cobra
6 So there
7 Beverly Hills
8 Idea
13 Bewitch
15 Biretta
17 Learn
18 Utah
20 Bream

44

Across:
1 Core
3 Shun (Caution)
9 Abide
10 Tradesman
11 Knead
12 Castigate
15 Muddle
17 Angela
19 Negotiate
21 Chart
23 Elemental
24 Utter
25 Nosh
26 Brio

Down:
1 Catacomb
2 Rhapsody
4 Hymnal
5 Nankeen
6 Pike
7 Bend
8 Peri
13 Decanter
14 Waterloo
16 Lantern
18 Egress
20 Tier
21 Coup
22 Alto

The Telegraph

Solutions 45–46

45

Across:
1 Shahs
4 Green (Shower screen)
10 Deposit
11 Gifts
12 Pasta
13 Altered
15 Name
17 Funds
19 Flush
22 Into
25 Plateau
27 Cared
29 Least
30 Skilful
31 Jeers
32 Agree

Down:
2 Hopes
3 Husband
5 Right
6 Efforts
7 Adept
8 Steam
9 Aside
14 Left
16 Asia
18 Unaware
20 Locking
21 Aptly
23 Nurse
24 Adult
26 Enter
28 Rifle

46

Across:
1 Kris
4 Tougher (Christopher)
8 Columbia
9 Run
11 Meagre
13 Future
14 Elvis
15 Apse
17 Derv
18 Paint
20 Suitor
21 Deja vu
24 Dot
25 Warranty
26 Renewed
27 Surf

Down:
2 Rioja
3 Square
4 Tube
5 Uranus
6 Hirsute
7 Rendezvous
10 Ambassador
12 Elgar
13 Fiend
16 Stilton
18 Powwow
19 Texans
22 Actor
23 Arid

Solutions 47-48

Across:
1 *Fee*
3 *Licks*
6 *Tow* (Felixstowe)
8 Icing
9 Suffolk
10 Stowmarket
12 Nut
15 Feud
17 Bury
18 Eye
22 Easy target
25 Ipswich
26 Ditto
27 Boy
28 Green
29 Nth

Down:
1 Fail-safe
2 Epilogue
3 Legume
4 Castro
5 Soften
6 Troy
7 Wake
11 Tub
13 Tungsten
14 Eyetooth
16 Dye
19 Ealing
20 Lychee
21 Walden
23 Limb
24 I-spy

Across:
1 *Noh*
3 *Ozark*
6 *Gnu*
8 *Tamar*
9 *Kneaded* (Noah's Ark: New tamer needed)
10 Bass singer
12 Ram
15 Emus
17 Tame
18 Net
22 Crocodiles
25 Journal
26 Birds
27 Roe
28 Satie
29 SOS

Down:
1 Notables
2 Homespun
3 Ogress
4 Asking
5 Keeper
6 Gods
7 Urdu
11 Rat
13 Mallards
14 Persists
16 Sec
19 Trunks
20 Ocelot
21 Edible
23 Ajar
24 Mule

Solutions 49–50

49

Across:
1 *Soil*
4 *Sun*
6 *Hit*
9 *Sin* (Solzhenitsyn)
10 Panic
11 Leave
12 Aubergine
15 Cash registers
19 Saturnine
21 Alibi
22 Bring
24 Arc
25 Say
26 Elk
27 Echo

Down:
2 Omnibus
3 Leper
4 Son
5 Nucleus
6 Human
7 Tame
8 Askance
13 Ingot
14 Essence
16 Risible
17 Epitaph
18 Dicey
20 Rogue
21 Aids
23 Irk

50

Across:
1 Sheikh
5 Spear (Shakespeare)
9 Hindsight
10 Rod
11 Spy
12 Polar bear
14 Elf
16 Digit
18 Tea
19 Funicular
21 Egg
22 Eta
23 Messenger
25 Dwell
26 Dither

Down:
2 Honey
3 Insipid
4 Hug
5 Satyr
6 Earnest
7 Rider Haggard
8 Chesterfield
13 Legal
15 Fanfare
17 Torrent
20 Camel
21 Eagle
24 Sad

Solutions 51–52

51

Across:
1 Balm
4 Aides (Barmaids)
8 Register
9 Idea
10 Late
11 Holsters
12 Senses
14 Waders
16 Receiver
19 Gets
20 Aged
21 Theatres
22 Rural
23 Test

Down:
2 Arise
3 Matches
4 Aural
5 Drifted
6 Spear
7 Relate
13 Slender
14 Warmest
15 Rotten
17 Eager
18 Vital
19 Gates

52

Across:
1 *A Level*
4 *Plane*
8 *Field* (A level playing field)
9 Omitted
10 Aquaria
11 Scar
12 Hub
14 Weed
15 Elba
18 Oak
21 Cage
23 Inexact
25 Origami
26 Adage
27 Lie-in
28 Report

Down:
1 Affray
2 Execute
3 El Dorado
4 Prig
5 Aztec
6 Endure
7 Jonah
13 Beverage
16 Bravado
17 School
19 Kiwis
20 Street
22 Guise
24 Pawn

The Telegraph

Solutions 53–54

53

Across:
1 *Exe*
3 *Pert*
5 *Ease* (Expertise)
8 Clear off
10 Just
11 Hod
13 Furze
14 Croissant
16 Ayr
17 Ufo
19 Far from it
21 Adieu
22 Shy
24 Oval
25 Misstate
26 Body
27 Twee
28 Kip

Down:
1 Etch
2 Eyed
3 Purposeful
4 Raffia
6 Aquarium
7 Entrepot
9 Lorry
12 Aftertaste
14 Catacomb
15 Ordinand
18 Fight
20 Review
22 Sack
23 Yelp

54

Across:
1 *Chine*
5 *Niece*
8 *Tikka*
9 *Weigh* (Chinese takeaway)
10 Immensely
11 Lot
12 Support team
15 Spreadsheet
19 Etc
20 Spaceship
22 India
23 Viola
24 Gooey
25 Nonet

Down:
1 Cowslips
2 Idiots
3 Ethiopia
4 Akimbo
5 Naan
6 Effete
7 Easy
13 Thespian
14 Merchant
16 Rialto
17 School
18 Tendon
20 Swag
21 Envy

Solutions 55–56

55

Across:
1 *Friends*
5 *Quiz*
7 *Scene* (French cuisine)
8 Chance
10 Iota
11 Pestered
13 Unable
14 Stroll
17 Forcible
19 Fete
21 Treaty
22 Drama
23 Clue
24 Resolve

Down:
1 Fisticuffs
2 Inertia
3 Need
4 Secret
5 Quantity
6 Incur
9 Adulterate
12 Ultimate
15 Overall
16 Player
18 Rural
20 Adds

56

Across:
1 Pharaoh
5 Ease (Faroese)
7 Resit
8 Copper
10 Imam
11 Moderate
13 Useful
14 Aspect
17 Alsatian
19 Wear
21 Barren
22 Adieu
23 Leap
24 Raleigh

Down:
1 Particular
2 Assuage
3 Anti
4 Hector
5 Espresso
6 Siena
9 See-through
12 Butter up
15 Emeriti
16 Banner
18 Stale
20 Fall

Solutions 57–58

57

Across:

1 *Monk*
4 *Ease*
8 *Hoot* (Monkey suit)
9 Classical
11 Carton
13 Centres
15 Grades
16 Strike
18 Spears
20 Enters
22 Engaged
23 Course
25 Telegraph
26 Will
27 Gets
28 Rent

Down:

2 Only
3 Kissed
4 Exists
5 Spaces
6 Contained
7 Stun
10 Lasting
12 Ages
13 Carefully
14 Nearest
17 Easy
19 Sneeze
20 Eaters
21 Terror
23 Cows
24 Open

58

Across:

7 Source
8 Errors (Sorcerers)
10 Re-reads
11 Banal
12 Crew
13 Greet
17 Frank
18 Moth
22 Liszt
23 Umpteen
24 Ice axe
25 Grotto

Down:

1 Ostrich
2 Quarter
3 Ocean
4 Problem
5 Joint
6 Psalm
9 Astronaut
14 Pretext
15 Novelty
16 Shannon
19 Plain
20 Usher
21 Spare

Solutions 59–60

59

Across:
7 Fourth
8 Wright (Forthright)
9 Nonsense verse
10 Adequate
12 Bide
13 Cute
15 Passer-by
17 Ghetto-blaster
19 Coyote
20 Fan-jet

Down:
1 Yo-yoed
2 Cross-question
3 When
4 Tweezers
5 Mixed blessing
6 Phased
11 Asphodel
14 Unhook
16 Brewed
18 Lift

60

Across:
1 Cru
3 Sea
5 Verb
7 Alice
8 Tickle (Cruciverbalistical)
10 Lair
11 Oratorio
13 Skylon
14 Sordid
17 Optimist
19 Acer
21 Dilute
22 Opera
23 Edge
24 Pun
25 Sad

Down:
1 Charleston
2 Utility
3 Shem
4 Asters
5 Vocation
6 Ruler
9 Wonderland
12 Dormouse
15 Duchess
16 Asleep
18 Triad
20 Moon

The Telegraph

Solutions 61–62

61

Across:
1 Hook
3 Airs (Who cares?)
9 Horse
10 Matrimony
11 Naked
12 Ceasefire
15 Drench
17 Assist
19 Blaspheme
21 Shrub
23 Lumbering
24 Chase
25 Rare
26 Myth

Down:
1 Homicide
2 Outdated
4 Ironic
5 Shyness
6 Trek
7 Dead
8 Dire
13 Fidelity
14 Strength
16 Cobbler
18 Hammer
20 Peek
21 Sack
22 Rear

62

Across:
1 Quarter
5 Rise (Cauterize)
7 Enter
8 Factor
10 Nice
11 Retrieve
13 Leeway
14 Centre
17 Negligee
19 Tuna
21 Danger
22 Audit
23 Star
24 Emperor

Down:
1 Queensland
2 Article
3 Tare
4 Rafter
5 Recorder
6 Store
9 Benefactor
12 Malinger
15 Thunder
16 Decree
18 Grant
20 Harp

Solutions 63–64

63

Across:
1 Country
5 Shun (Contrition)
7 Route
8 Lactic
10 Loud
11 Befriend
13 Silver
14 Stanza
17 Lowlands
19 Brat
21 Garage
22 Icing
23 Fete
24 Twinges

Down:
1 Carelessly
2 Unusual
3 Trek
4 Yelled
5 Security
6 Unite
9 Advantages
12 Separate
15 Nursing
16 Advert
18 Whale
20 Kiwi

64

Across:
1 Hiker
4 Manned (High command)
9 Jubilee
10 Taper
11 Calf
12 Require
13 Moa
14 Epee
16 Ella
18 Gas
20 Warrior
21 Spur
24 Tunic
25 Victory
26 Hornet
27 Style

Down:
1 HIJack
2 Kabul
3 Rule
5 Antiques
6 Nuptial
7 Dorset
8 Zebra
13 Mediocre
15 Partner
17 Switch
18 Grave
19 Groyne
22 Proxy
23 Aces

The Telegraph

Solutions 65-66

65

Across:
1 *Fork*
4 *Lows*
8 *Sure* (Foreclosure)
9 By no means
11 Dancer
13 Piraeus
15 Finney
16 Physic
18 Taurus
20 Sneeze
22 Stopgap
23 Avatar
25 Lookalike
26 Axis
27 Fern
28 Tote

Down:
2 Oryx
3 Kaolin
4 Leeway
5 Wind up
6 Quickstep
7 Fear
10 Sashing
12 E-fit
13 Pneumatic
14 Refusal
17 Chef
19 Strove
20 Spoken
21 Eaglet
23 Ajar
24 Skit

66

Across:
1 *Hip*
3 *Hippo*
6 *Ray* (Hip-hip-hooray)
8 Cheer
9 Overlap
10 Suspicious
12 Pap
15 Espy
17 Gale
18 Sob
22 Blackguard
25 Classic
26 Churl
27 Mad
28 Sheep
29 Yam

Down:
1 Huckster
2 Press-ups
3 Heroic
4 Profit
5 Open up
6 Role
7 Yips
11 Sag
13 Paraguay
14 Pendulum
16 Yob
19 Blasts
20 Icicle
21 Eggcup
23 Scam
24 Card

Solutions 67–68

67

Across:
1 Sigh
4 Gone (Saigon)
8 Poke
9 Allowance
11 Knight
13 Deleted
15 Barrel
16 Double
18 Excuse
20 Aspire
22 Unclean
23 Ignore
25 Erroneous
26 Okay
27 Cyst
28 Take

Down:
2 Idle
3 Hoover
4 Gravel
5 Nicked
6 Hobgoblin
7 Seat
10 Endorse
12 Able
13 Draconian
14 Leisure
17 Ever
19 Energy
20 Almost
21 Patent
23 Icon
24 Dusk

68

Across:
1 Feint
4 Prays (Faint praise)
8 Elk
9 Bullfighter
10 Egghead
12 Child
13 Normal
14 Bestow
17 Sober
19 Emblems
21 Livingstone
23 Add
24 Ideal
25 Yokel

Down:
1 Fable
2 Ill
3 Taffeta
4 Pagoda
5 Attic
6 Serviette
7 Skiddaw
11 Garibaldi
13 Nosegay
15 Embassy
16 Fennel
18 Revue
20 Spell
22 Oak

The Telegraph

Solutions 69–70

69

Across:
1 *High*
3 *Dance*
7 *Sikh* (Hide and seek)
8 Retrievers
9 Aids
12 Rift valleys
13 Mumps
15 Sweat
19 Anaesthetic
21 Data
23 Terra firma
24 Pint
25 Yield
26 Guts

Down:
1 Horn-rimmed
2 Hardtop
3 Deejay
4 Needle
5 Essay
6 Skid
10 Isle
11 Santa Claus
14 Moat
16 Weeping
17 Degree
18 Strand
20 Natty
22 Aria

70

Across:
1 *Ban*
3 *Key*
5 *Moon* (Ban Ki-moon)
7 Liver
8 Siskin
10 Half
11 Petulant
13 Zoom in
14 Stream
17 Arsonist
19 Data
21 Temple
22 Ad lib
23 Crag
24 Mix
25 Dim

Down:
1 Belshazzar
2 Novello
3 Kerb
4 Yes-men
5 Mosquito
6 Ouija
9 Stamp album
12 Winnipeg
15 Enabled
16 Esteem
18 Swear
20 Marx

Solutions 71–72

71

Across:
1 *Torn*
4 *Knee*
8 *Howl* (Tawny owl)
9 Spoonbill
11 Aegean
13 Closing
15 Breech
16 Dipper
18 Siskin
20 Slalom
22 Pink-eye
23 Tut-tut
25 Truncated
26 Know
27 Achy
28 Edda

Down:
2 Oops
3 Noodle
4 Kibosh
5 Elland
6 Love-apple
7 Glen
10 Legible
12 Ibis
13 Cessation
14 Occiput
17 Rump
19 Nitric
20 Skinny
21 Aye-aye
23 Tyke
24 Fend

72

Across:
1 *Gnash*
4 *Veal*
8 *Sin*
9 *Tennessee* (Nashville's in Tennessee)
10 AWOL
11 Activity
12 Ore
13 Secure
14 Magnus
16 Ran
17 Credited
18 Etna
20 Elevators
21 Odd
22 Lynn
23 Rusty

Down:
1 Gas bags
2 Anne of Cleves
3 Hits
4 Venice
5 American
6 Assignations
7 Sexy
11 Are
12 Ordinary
14 Mad
15 Stand by
16 Renown
17 Cleo
19 User

The Telegraph

Solutions 73–74

73

Across:
1 Penny
5 Trait (Penetrate)
8 Obese
9 Utter
10 Knowledge
11 Eye
12 Good-natured
15 Expenditure
19 Met
20 Labyrinth
22 Farce
23 Corfu
24 Teeth
25 Leeds

Down:
1 Prudence
2 Nutmeg
3 Yorktown
4 Heroin
5 Tell
6 Agadir
7 Tome
13 Truthful
14 Distress
16 Pebble
17 Ignore
18 Emerge
20 Lost
21 Rich

74

Across:
1 Bored
4 Rheum (Boardroom)
8 Ash
9 Syndication
10 Swindle
12 Exact
13 Rapier
14 Twitch
17 Scrub
19 Parsnip
21 In character
23 Tea
24 Lenin
25 Tinge

Down:
1 Basis
2 Run
3 Dwindle
4 Reader
5 Elite
6 Manhattan
7 Cheetah
11 Impartial
13 Risotto
15 Warrant
16 Sprain
18 Bacon
20 Purge
22 Tan

Solutions 75–76

75

Across:
1 Cough
4 Hiccups (Coffee cups)
8 Axe
9 Pests
10 Adopted
11 Collecting
14 Treaty
16 Adults
18 Illustrate
22 Tourist
23 Thumb
24 Ail
25 Manager
26 Enemy

Down:
1 Capacity
2 Unsolved
3 Haste
4 Health
5 Crowned
6 Up to
7 Side
12 Pleasure
13 Assembly
15 Telling
17 Guitar
19 Title
20 Stem
21 Burn

76

Across:
1 Bawl
3 Bering (Ball bearing)
9 Kindest
10 Viand
11 Rib
12 Dripstone
13 Sprout
14 Fracas
16 Injurious
19 Tan
21 Exude
22 Muezzin
23 Detest
24 Gnat

Down:
1 Baker
2 Wine bar
4 Elvis Presley
5 Idaho
6 Goddess
7 Headquarters
8 Etui
13 Stipend
15 Citizen
17 Joust
18 Ohms
20 Nonet

The Telegraph

Solutions 77–78

77

Across:
1 *Neville*
8 *Chamber*
9 *Laine* (Neville Chamberlain)
10 Transcend
11 Ode
12 Rider
13 Peter
14 Jeans
16 David
19 Oar
20 Sessional
22 Irish
23 Plectra
24 Rancour

Down:
1 Nelson
2 Vainer
3 Lee tides
4 Eclair
5 Pass
6 Abject
7 Trader
13 Pavilion
14 Joseph
15 Austen
16 Dunbar
17 Domino
18 Arthur
21 Iota

78

Across:
1 *No one*
4 *Reeds*
10 *Cereals*
11 *Today* (No one reads serials today)
12 Ensue
13 Azaleas
15 Sumo
17 Flats
19 Obese
22 Emma
25 Deronda
27 Rebus
29 Adler
30 Minogue
31 Titan
32 Stays

Down:
2 Orris
3 Nearest
5 Extra
6 Dodgers
7 Acted
8 Assam
9 Gypsy
14 Zoom
16 Used
18 Lorelei
20 Baronet
21 Ideal
23 Mammy
24 Essex
26 Norma
28 Bogey

Solutions 79-80

79

Across:
1 *Madder*
4 *Cask*
9 *Err* (Madagascar)
10 Undergone
11 Leering
12 Whine
13 Creed
15 Dregs
20 Order
22 Rampant
24 Encounter
25 Gap
26 Lady
27 Legend.

Down:
1 Meekly
2 Dirge
3 Erudite
5 Arrow
6 Knowing
7 Adage
8 Bevel
14 Radical
16 Remorse
17 Money
18 Trite
19 Stupid
21 Round
23 Argue

80

Across:
1 Rites
4 Tough (Right stuff)
10 Cheaper
11 Dance
12 Tests
13 Physics
15 Easy
17 Sheds
19 Mules
22 King
25 Compass
27 Lower
29 Opera
30 Useless
31 After
32 State

Down:
2 Ideas
3 Exposed
5 Oddly
6 Genuine
7 Acute
8 Wraps
9 Sense
14 Hymn
16 Asks
18 Himself
20 Ugliest
21 Actor
23 Issue
24 Trust
26 Awake
28 Wheat

Solutions 81–82

81

Across:
1 Hike
3 Ought (High court)
7 Role
8 Plasticine
9 Aunt
12 Experiments
13 Irony
15 Basin
19 Educational
21 Sure
23 Lieutenant
24 Sofa
25 Yield
26 Slid

Down:
1 Happenings
2 Eastern
3 Origin
4 Gained
5 Treat
6 Plan
10 Uses
11 Translated
14 Over
16 Amounts
17 Scheme
18 Stated
20 Delay
22 Upon

82

Across:
1 Folder
4 Hole (Folderol)
9 Khaki
10 Wyoming
11 Rosette
12 Obese
13 Junket
15 Osiris
18 Lemur
20 Assists
23 Pageant
24 Squat
25 Coke
26 Glider

Down:
1 Fakir
2 Liaison
3 Evict
5 Odorous
6 Exile
7 Sweet
8 Ogress
13 Jalopy
14 Earmark
16 Resound
17 Waltz
19 Magic
21 Sisal
22 Sitar

Solutions 83-84

83

Across:
1 *Sir*
3 *Kit*
5 *Bray*
7 *Curse* (Circuit breakers)
8 Cloudy
10 Hobo
11 Electric
13 Ratify
14 Sloven
17 Nuthatch
19 Proa
21 Pundit
22 Bingo
23 Spin
24 Hay
25 Ass

Down:
1 Saccharine
2 Rarebit
3 Keep
4 Tackle
5 Broccoli
6 Adder
9 Scandalous
12 Off-and-on
15 Veranda
16 Scotch
18 Thump
20 Obey

84

Across:
1 *Wether*
4 *Profit*
9 *Sikhs*
10 *Fir-cone* (Weather prophet seeks fir-cone)
11 Eat
12 Elman
13 Eclogue
15 Stand by your
19 Cruiser
20 Potty
21 Noh
22 On-drive
24 Opera
25 Sundry
26 Horses

Down:
1 Wisden
2 Takamatsu
3 Essen
5 Rurally
6 Fro
7 Teeter
8 Afterburner
14 Gauntlets
16 Nastier
17 Actors
18 Bypass
20 Photo
23 Don

Solutions 85–86

85

Across:
4 Plaice
5 Mann (Placeman)
7 Andorra
9 Dirty
10 Nun
11 Web
13 Proof
15 Startle
16 Adieu
17 Cry
18 Ark
21 Genre
22 Knees-up
23 Tutu
24 Fiasco

Down:
1 Baron
2 Acorn
3 Calibre
4 Pang
6 Notion
8 Rupture
9 Deplore
12 Orb
14 Advent
15 Secrete
18 Anvil
19 Kelso
20 Judo

86

Across:
1 More
4 Gait (Moorgate)
8 Ogre
9 Geriatric
11 Ordeal
13 Silence
15 Boater
16 Yeomen
18 Adroit
20 Pernod
22 Cabaret
23 Symbol
25 Nefarious
26 Mini
27 Stay
28 Shun (Station)

Down:
2 Over
3 Elicit
4 Gather
5 Idiocy
6 Agreement
7 Deal
10 Creeper
12 Abba
13 Sacrament
14 Lexicon
17 Nude
19 Talent
20 Papacy
21 Remiss
23 Semi
24 Tutu

Solutions 87–88

87

Across:
1 Freeze
5 Peach (Free speech)
9 Separates
10 Ova
11 Odd
12 Classroom
14 Ire
16 Edged
18 Yes
19 Hopefully
21 Far
22 Era
23 Keyboards
25 Tends
26 Pokier

Down:
2 Roped
3 Earache
4 Eat
5 Posts
6 Apology
7 Headmistress
8 Astonishment
13 Angel
15 Explain
17 Dry dock
20 Fakes
21 Force
24 Yap

88

Across:
1 *Inn*
3 *Ten*
5 *City* (Intensity)
7 Quite
8 De luxe
10 Item
11 Mediocre
13 Idylls
14 Frozen
17 Objected
19 Talc
21 Discus
22 Moose
23 Heap
24 Sag
25 Shy

Down:
1 Inquisitor
2 Naively
3 Twee
4 Nudged
5 Colliery
6 Toxic
9 Pernickety
12 Blackcap
15 Zealous
16 Census
18 Juice
20 Smug

Solutions 89–90

89

Across:
1 *Per*
3 *Lea*
5 *Gaits* (Pearly gates)
8 Rigid
9 St Peter
10 Hell
11 One by one
13 Heaven
14 Nicety
17 Sidereal
19 Myth
22 Inferno
23 Bliss
24 Hades
25 Fad
26 May

Down:
1 Parch
2 Regalia
3 Lady
4 Assent
5 Go public
6 Intro
7 Sorcery
12 Bear arms
13 Hashish
15 Elysium
16 Lay off
18 Dyfed
20 Husky
21 Abed

90

Across:
1 *Jaw-jaw*
4 *Welles*
7 *Wigan Pier* (George Orwell's 'Wigan Pier')
9 Buhl
10 Rock
11 Curry
13 Sits up
14 Sedans
15 Sahibs
17 Stucco
19 Salts
20 Talk
22 Snip
23 Lightning
24 Vestry
25 Eighty

Down:
1 Jumbos
2 Jail
3 Wrap up
4 Wipers
5 Leer
6 Stokes
7 Whitehall
8 Romancing
11 Curbs
12 Yeats
15 Satnav
16 Sashay
17 Stance
18 Osprey
21 Kilt
22 Snog

Solutions 91–92

91

Across:
1 Bode
5 Lair (Baudelaire)
7 Asinine
8 Dethrone
10 Gasp
12 Cult
14 Hogshead
16 Gangster
17 Nail
18 Zest
19 Criminal
22 Fxploit
23 Over
24 Acme

Down:
1 Bald
2 Each
3 Ricochet
4 Wise
5 Lengthen
6 Rump
9 Educate
11 Stamina
13 Together
15 Garrison
18 Zero
19 Cape
20 Iota
21 Lure

92

Across:
1 Monarch
5 Rome
7 Photo
8 Graphs (Monochrome photographs)
10 Ibid
11 Closeted
13 Go hang
14 Logjam
17 Unctuous
19 Quin
21 Sleaze
22 Ranee
23 Axle
24 Sky-blue

Down:
1 Mapping out
2 Neolith
3 Rook
4 Haggle
5 Roadshow
6 My hat
9 Adam and Eve
12 Insulate
15 Journal
16 Duress
18 Calyx
20 Fray

Solutions 93–94

93

Across:
1 Belief
5 Flops (Belly flops)
9 Passports
10 Vet
11 Ray
12 Occasions
14 Caw
16 Event
18 Spa
19 Automatic
21 Wit
22 Ire
23 Surrender
25 Nasty
26 Desire

Down:
2 Essay
3 Improve
4 Far
5 Fasts
6 Obvious
7 Satisfactory
8 Appreciation
13 Chest
15 Witness
17 Tickers
20 Misty
21 Wader
24 Rid

94

Across:
1 Quay
4 Tones (Key tones)
8 Apres-ski
9 Vole
10 Bass
11 Magellan
12 Remark
14 Amazon
16 Jingoism
19 Cuff
20 Limb
21 Sinecure
22 Twain
23 Styx

Down:
2 Users
3 Yashmak
4 Thing
5 Novella
6 Salsa
7 Opiate
13 Algebra
14 Almonds
15 Oxford
17 Idiot
18 Ibsen
19 Cocky

Solutions 95–96

95

Across:

1 *Knew*
4 *Moan*
8 *Near* (Pneumonia)
9 Fruitlets
11 Homage
13 Chiasma
15 Blotch
16 Angina
18 Entice
20 Assign
22 Onerous
23 Regale
25 Drumstick
26 Poop
27 Eyas
28 Yank

Down:

2 Norm
3 Weight
4 Mullah
5 Asthma
6 Hepatitis
7 Urge
10 So-and-so
12 Able
13 Contagion
14 Ice-cold
17 Acne
19 Energy
20 Aramis
21 Sultry
23 Rope
24 Scan

96

Across:

1 *Moats*
4 *Herts*
8 *Ave*
9 *Verum Corpus* (Mozart's Ave Verum Corpus)
10 Esquire
12 Dress
13 Praise
14 Rosary
17 Vital
19 Catch up
21 Rest in peace
23 Tee
24 Dares
25 Earls

Down:

1 Movie
2 Air
3 Summits
4 Hoover
5 Rapid
6 Sassenach
7 Debussy
11 Quartered
13 Poverty
15 Octuple
16 Scrips
18 Laser
20 Peers
22 Ayr

Solutions 97–98

97

Across:
1 Beat
4 Route (Beetroot)
8 Hygienic
9 Duty
10 Spry
11 Ice cream
12 Jargon
14 Loofah
16 Warranty
19 Boon
20 Tiff
21 Colossal
22 Suede
23 Yolk

Down:
2 Edify
3 Tension
4 Recce
5 Undergo
6 Extra
7 Myopia
13 Giraffe
14 Loyalty
15 Anorak
17 Alias
18 Niche
19 Basil

98

Across:
7 Serial
8 Packet (Cereal packet)
9 Arachnophobia
10 Commence
12 Leek
13 Part
15 Glycerol
17 Countenancing
19 Desert
20 Agents

Down:
1 Weirdo
2 Circumstances
3 Clan
4 Apoplexy
5 Schoolteacher
6 Feline
11 Neglects
14 Apogee
16 Ornate
18 Away

Solutions 99–100

99

Across:
1 Alack
4 Heart (A la carte)
10 Mineral
11 Recap
12 Cargo
13 Pirates
15 Tied
17 Feast
19 Least
22 Even
25 Outcome
27 Depth
29 Linen
30 Useless
31 Study
32 Asked

Down:
2 Lunar
3 Carrots
5 Error
6 Recites
7 Smack
8 Slope
9 Spasm
14 Idle
16 Item
18 Extinct
20 Endless
21 Noble
23 Venus
24 Phase
26 Owned
28 Piece

100

Across:
1 Awry
3 Tangle (A right angle)
9 Cop shop
10 Quota
11 Tin
12 Permanent
13 Badger
14 Indeed
16 Melodrama
19 Erg
21 Skimp
22 Archive
23 Dryden
24 Flue

Down:
1 Ascot
2 Repined
4 Acquaintance
5 Grove
6 Exacted
7 Shepherd's pie
8 Spur
13 Bemused
15 Ezekiel
17 Laity
18 Ajax
20 Glebe

Solutions 101–102

101

Across:
1 *Speed*
4 *March*
8 *Ant* (Speed merchant)
9 Accelerator
10 Impress
12 Dream
13 Ersatz
14 Adjust
17 Ether
19 Advance
21 Subtracting
23 Tot
24 Esker
25 Thyme

Down:
1 Swazi
2 Etc
3 Diluent
4 Morose
5 Rated
6 Harlequin
7 Attempt
11 Posthaste
13 Execute
15 Dovecot
16 Fairer
18 Rubik
20 Eagle
22 Ivy

102

Across:
1 *Sailor*
4 *Waiter*
9 *Cedar*
10 *Whirled* (Sail away to see the world)
11 Ire
12 Rules
13 Noodles
15 Sell-by dates
19 October
20 Fence
21 Ace
22 Sporran
24 Miami
25 Taiwan
26 Writhe

Down:
1 Secure
2 Indulgent
3 Orris
5 Arizona
6 Tal
7 Rudest
8 Twenty grand
14 Lie in wait
16 Liberia
17 Dorset
18 Venice
20 Femur
23 Obi

Solutions 103–104

103

Across:
1 *Bow*
3 *Dull*
5 *Hair* (Baudelaire)
8 Atrocity
10 Opus
11 Ton
13 Learn
14 Pertinent
16 Ere
17 Sin
19 Abhorrent
21 Count
22 Sew
24 Fire
25 Mediocre
26 Last
27 Stun
28 Nip

Down:
1 Beat
2 Worn
3 Decapitate
4 Little
6 Applause
7 Resonant
9 Tower
12 Alteration
14 Peaceful
15 Requires
18 Infer
20 Honest
22 Scan
23 Weep

104

Across:
1 Bears
4 Soles (Bare souls)
10 Careful
11 Dairy
12 Layer
13 Pirates
15 Eats
17 Acted
19 Needs
22 Data
25 Compass
27 Grasp
29 Agent
30 Dirtier
31 Metre
32 Types

Down:
2 Early
3 Referee
5 Order
6 Existed
7 Scale
8 Slept
9 Gypsy
14 Isn't
16 Adds
18 Compete
20 Eagerly
21 Ocean
23 Aside
24 Opera
26 After
28 Alive

The Telegraph

Solutions 105–106

105

Across:
1 Fright
5 Reign (Freight train)
9 Countless
10 Fan
11 Owe
12 Esperanto
14 Pal
16 Snarl
18 Yam
19 Ingenious
21 Act
22 Hub
23 Soap opera
25 Dwell
26 Entrap

Down:
2 Rouse
3 Gathers
4 Toe
5 Riser
6 Infancy
7 Non-committal
8 Accomplished
13 Piano
15 Legible
17 Lose out
20 Nasal
21 Arena
24 Ale

106

Across:
1 Jester
4 Moment
  (Just a moment)
7 Moussaka
9 Absinth
12 Syria
13 Vapid
15 Oldie
16 Indus
17 Dicta
18 Toper
19 Ellipse
23 Taciturn
24 Fellow
25 Recess

Down:
1 James Joyce
2 Square deal
3 Enslaved
4 Moab
5 Magi
6 Next
8 Kampuchea
10 Nom de plume
11 Hamstrings
14 Diatribe
20 Laze
21 Idol
22 Stew

Solutions 107–108

107

Across:
1 *Cell*
3 *Bide*
9 *Eight* (Sell-by date)
10 Moraliser
11 Index
12 Task force
15 Squash
17 Italic
19 Juxtapose
21 Photo
23 Ufologist
24 Razor
25 Nude
26 Deep

Down:
1 Comatose
2 Larkspur
4 Insure
5 Eeriest
6 Aged
7 Styx
8 Clef
13 Fluorine
14 Screwtop
16 Sojourn
18 Oxford
20 Avow
21 Pork
22 Ooze

108

Across:
1 *Sissy*
4 *Fuss*
7 *Hill*
8 *Climbing*
9 *Sensation* (Sisyphus, hill-climbing sensation!)
10 Awl
12 Isomer
14 Ordeal
16 Ash
18 Wednesday
21 Boulders
22 e-Bay
23 Zeus
24 Asset

Down:
1 Shiners
2 Selfsame
3 Yacht
4 Fibs
5 Sinew
6 Kimono
11 Odysseus
13 Reefer
15 Adamant
17 Stone
19 Nessa
20 Alas

The Telegraph

Solutions 109–110

109

Across:
1 Moor
3 Titian (Mortician)
9 Neptune
10 Twist
11 Roe
12 Performer
13 Castro
14 Cudgel
16 Assailant
19 Ill
21 Track
22 Sponsor
23 Riddle
24 Lyre

Down:
1 Manor
2 Orpheus
4 Introduction
5 Idiom
6 Natural
7 Pumpernickel
8 Dear
13 Coaster
15 Grimsby
17 Stand
18 Also
20 Large

110

Across:
1 Wren
3 Wire (Renoir)
9 Niece
10 Initiated
11 Lento
12 Tolerance
15 Easter
17 Asthma
19 Iconology
21 Braid
23 Emphysema
24 Alien
25 Tale
26 Used

Down:
1 Whistles
2 Evillest
4 Intent
5 Endless
6 Dean
7 Zero
8 Pier
13 Theorems
14 Maryland
16 Evident
18 Compel
20 Onyx
21 Beat
22 Adit

Solutions 111-112

Across:
1 Affair
4 Retail (A fairy tale)
7 Prospect
9 Replied
12 Error
13 Title
15 Issue
16 Swede
17 Ducat
18 Opium
19 Endless
23 Ambition
24 Credit
25 Angels

Down:
1 Appreciate
2 Flourished
3 Imported
4 Rate
5 Toil
6 Idle
8 Criticism
10 Indefinite
11 Determines
14 Estonian
20 Near
21 Load
22 Salt

111

Across:
1 Cede
4 Potato (Seed potato)
7 Nee
9 Jusl
10 Tiresome
11 Eve
12 Oven
13 Rhodesia
16 Screenwriters
19 Stiffest
23 Mask
24 Imp
25 Boarding
26 Tiny
27 Hoe
28 Septet
29 Deed

Down:
2 Equivocation
3 Entente
4 Peter
5 Torso
6 Taste
8 Omnipresence
14 Howls
15 Dai
17 Elf
18 Tempted
20 Furze
21 Exist
22 Tight

112

The Telegraph

Solutions 113–114

113

Across:
1 *How*
3 *Swarming*
9 *Party* (House-warming party)
10 Illegal
11 Tax
13 Xenophobe
14 Galaxy
16 Verity
18 Alpha test
20 Gee
22 Exotica
23 Xebec
25 Energise
26 Pal

Down:
1 Hop it
2 War
4 Whinny
5 Relapse
6 Ingrowing
7 Gallery
8 Lynx
12 Xylophone
14 Glad eye
15 X-raying
17 Le Mans
19 Text
21 Excel
24 Bap

114

Across:
1 *Sonia*
4 *Temper*
9 *Hairy*
10 *Setback*
11 *Shirley* (It's only a temporary setback, surely!)
12 Notes
14 Out
15 Ego
16 Ult
18 Par
21 Upper
22 Limoges
23 Magenta
25 Obama
26 Trygon
27 Ha-has

Down:
1 Schism
2 Nailing up
3 Any Old
5 Extent
6 PGA
7 Rakish
8 Use your loaf
13 Telegraph
17 Summit
18 Pronto
19 Smooth
20 Essays
24 Guy. Thanks, Steve and Lonny ...

Solutions 115–116

115

Across:
1 Pawn
3 Human (Paul Newman)
7 Unit
8 Unscripted
9 Gala
12 Degenerated
13 Roast
15 Besom
19 Superlative
21 Goon
23 Woodworker
24 Glue
25 Deter
26 Laic

Down:
1 Plundering
2 Nucleus
3 Hailed
4 Mutual
5 Nudge
6 Girl
10 Adds
11 Asymmetric
14 Also
16 Enthral
17 Devout
18 Glower
20 Unwed
22 Oily

116

Across:
1 Bull
3 Lingerie (Boulangerie)
9 Beano
10 Leading
11 Yes
13 Koala bear
14 Eunuch
16 Gyrate
18 Scavenger
20 Nip
22 Exotica
23 Newsy
25 Nightjar
26 A-one

Down:
1 Bobby
2 Lea
4 I'll say
5 Granary
6 Raise Cain
7 En garde
8 Dock
12 Singalong
14 Epstein
15 Chemist
17 Iguana
19 Rung
21 Payee
24 Who

The Telegraph

Solutions 117–118

117

Across:
1 Thud
4 Depend (The deep end)
7 Ore
9 Spin
10 Branches
11 Kit
12 Rove
13 Sentries
16 Consideration
19 Patients
23 Army
24 Arc
25 Question
26 Hang
27 Die
28 Recess
29 Rust

Down:
2 Hippopotamus
3 Donkeys
4 Debts
5 Plain
6 Nicer
8 Developments
14 Event
15 Tea
17 Ice
18 Teacher
20 Issue
21 Noise
22 Sands

118

Across:
4 Bawled
5 Tire (Bald tyre)
7 Creates
10 Troop
11 Karachi
12 Issue
14 Against
15 Quell
16 Kennels
20 Plead
21 Treason
22 Twit
23 Zombie

Down:
1 Tweak
2 Fever
3 Diarist
4 Bury
6 Exodus
8 Tangled
9 Salient
10 Thistle
13 Mullet
14 Alkalis
17 Error
18 Samba
19 Joke

Solutions 119-120

119

120

The Telegraph

Solutions 121–122

121

Across:
1 Stay
5 Bull (Stable)
7 Elevate
8 Bulletin
10 Pest
12 Cute
14 Souvenir
16 Suspense
17 Exam
18 Pyre
19 Straight
22 Syringe
23 Demo
24 Milk

Down:
1 Stab
2 Yell
3 Jettison
4 Gain
5 Bel paese
6 Lilt
9 Uruguay
11 Spinach
13 Espresso
15 Unerring
18 Pond
19 Serb
20 Item
21 Tusk

122

Across:
1 Reeds
4 Mined (Reads mind)
10 Whisper
11 Image
12 Noses
13 Scholar
15 Into
17 Spite
19 Daddy
22 Ages
25 Royalty
27 Seven
29 Union
30 Simpler
31 Aside
32 Added

Down:
2 Exits
3 Deposit
5 Irish
6 Enabled
7 Swing
8 Trust
9 Weary
14 Code
16 Neat
18 Physics
20 Assumed
21 Trout
23 Gypsy
24 Angry
26 Lined
28 Value

Solutions 123-124

123

Across:
1 Missed
5 Aches (Mistakes)
9 Escalator
10 Bet
11 Oar
12 Nurseries
14 Sum
16 Elder
18 Sea
19 Incorrect
21 Hat
22 Use
23 Professor
25 Emend
26 Litter

Down:
2 Incur
3 Silence
4 Dot
5 Agree
6 Hybrids
7 Satisfactory
8 Reconstitute
13 Ridge
15 Machete
17 Retreat
20 Roped
21 Haste
24 Owl

124

Across:
1 Lunette
5 Ticks (Lunatics)
8 Creep
9 Uncivil
10 Magically
12 Rue
13 Wangle
14 Escort
17 Oaf
18 Bottoms up
20 Pretext
21 Rioja
23 Rated
24 Electra

Down:
1 Locum
2 Née
3 Topical
4 Equals
5 Tacky
6 Cavernous
7 Solvent
11 Genuflect
13 Whopper
15 Scourge
16 Statue
18 Bread
19 Plaza
22 Out

The Telegraph

Solutions 125–126

125

Across:
1 Obstacle
8 Coarse (Obstacle course)
9 Bijoux
10 Show a leg
11 Eschew
13 Antedate
17 Chestnut
20 Hinder
23 Grey mare
25 Risqué
26 Flying
27 Aldermen

Down:
2 Bliss
3 Tooth
4 Coxswain
5 Echo
6 Hazard
7 Aspect
11 Epic
12 Cake
14 Tethered
15 Acid
16 Ever
18 Hurdle
19 Stymie
21 Noser
22 Elude
24 Alga

126

Across:
1 Rein
4 Boat
8 Rout (Rainbow trout)
9 Plausible
11 Errand
13 Cashier
15 Seethe
16 Parted
18 On time
20 Fierce
22 Panicky
23 Orator
25 Offshoots
26 A bit
27 Flea
28 Ting

Down:
2 Eels
3 Nougat
4 Blithe
5 Asleep
6 Monastery
7 Stud
10 Erratic
12 Oslo
13 C'est la vie
14 Shampoo
17 Deed
19 Earful
20 Fiesta
21 Eke out
23 Oral
24 Stun

Solutions 127–128

127

Across:
1 *Azure*
4 *Lie*
6 *Kit* (As You Like It)
8 Righteousness
9 Arena
11 Dope
13 Shame
14 Barmy
15 Rural
16 Hell
18 Alert
21 Dispassionate
23 Nun
24 Top
25 Podgy

Down:
1 Afraid
2 Urge
3 Extra
4 Loo
5 Ecstasy
6 Keepsake
7 Tussle
10 Eerie
12 Partisan
14 Blatant
15 Redden
17 Lonely
19 Troop
20 Hard
22 Sup

128

Across:
1 Bred
3 Bored (Bread board)
7 Inch
8 Noblewoman
9 Gone
12 Vermination
13 Lilac
15 Dream
19 Spectacular
21 Tree
23 Convenient
24 Gala
25 Nicks
26 Ever

Down:
1 Benevolent
2 Dilemma
3 Bowing
4 Remote
5 Dingo
6 Icon
10 Once
11 Enumerator
14 Lose
16 Routine
17 Scenic
18 Caress
20 Pecan
22 Rear

Solutions 129–130

129

Across:

1 Eyesore
5 Quay (Ice hockey)
7 Fleet
8 Prizes
10 Cage
11 Pocketed
13 Ending
14 Insure
17 Criminal
19 Dirt
21 Dental
22 Choir
23 Used
24 Parents

Down:

1 Efficiency
2 Emerged
3 Oath
4 Employ
5 Quickens
6 Agent
9 Adventures
12 Insisted
15 Unicorn
16 Gallop
18 Ideas
20 Scar

130

Across:

1 Take up
4 Hart (Take apart)
9 Types
10 Overeat
11 Stilton
12 Auden
13 Fights
15 Odessa
18 Chasm
20 Expound
23 Lenient
24 Delft
25 Lute
26 Leader

Down:

1 Titus
2 Kipling
3 Upset
5 Abelard
6 Tweed
7 Joint
8 Stanza
13 Facile
14 Tempest
16 Squalid
17 Petty
19 Annul
21 Padre
22 Deter

Solutions 131–132

131

Across:
1 *Hindi*
4 *Anne*
8 *Sub*
9 *Continent* (Indian subcontinent)
10 Iraq
11 Wolfgang
12 Van
13 Sidled
14 Old boy
16 Axe
17 Casualty
18 Clan
20 Carnivore
21 Tit
22 Once
23 Terse

Down:
1 His nibs
2 Nubian Desert
3 Inca
4 Amnion
5 Nail-file
6 Perambulator
7 Stag
11 Wad
12 Venation
14 Oxy
15 Yangtze
16 Al home
17 Cock
19 Jest

132

Across:
1 Cooker
7 Borough (Kookaburra)
8 Parallax
9 Ogled
10 Uncut
11 Dive
12 Amass
15 Dural
16 Daddy
19 Real
20 Awake
21 Satyr
22 Laughing
23 Jackass
24 Zoomed

Down:
1 Captured
2 On record
3 Eilat
4 Fox
5 Dodgem
6 Egress
7 Banderillas
9 Oval
13 Aquarium
14 Saw-edged
15 Dyer
17 Ararat
18 Dry ski
20 Anglo
22 LSD

The Telegraph

Solutions 133–134

133

Across:
1 Beech
4 Bawl (Beach ball)
8 Bacardi
9 Acute
10 Excel
11 Freesia
13 Aboard
15 Period
17 Awesome
20 Annoy
22 Olive
23 Amiable
24 Sect
25 Emend

Down:
1 Bible
2 Encyclopedia
3 Hurdler
4 Brief
5 Weave
6 Questionable
7 Herald
12 Rap
13 Amazon
14 Dam
16 Evasive
18 Obese
19 Exalt
21 Yield

134

Across:
1 Death
3 Thrown (Dethrone)
7 Cream puff
9 Boot
10 Tail
11 Straw
13 Eskimo
14 Third
15 Check
17 As it is
20 Kiosk
21 Blow
23 Flaw
24 Paso doble
25 Scotch
26 Anger

Down:
1 Double
2 Tort
3 Top-hat
4 Raft
5 Noble
6 Canto
7 Cock-a-hoop
8 Fairy tale
11 Smack
12 Whisk
16 Kibosh
17 Ascot
18 Sawyer
19 Abyss
22 Watt
23 Flan

Solutions 135–136

135

136

Solutions 137–138

137

Across:

1 *Four*
3 *Sight*
7 *Saga* (Forsyte Saga)
8 Chinchilla
9 Rhea
12 Parson's nose
13 Wispy
15 Booze
19 Ejector-seat
21 Raze
23 Equestrian
24 Kelp
25 Split
26 Else

Down:

1 Face-powder
2 Rings up
3 Sphinx
4 Galena
5 Tsars
6 Ogle
10 Hero
11 Acceptance
14 Suez
16 Observe
17 Actual
18 Cosset
20 Jeeps
22 Amen

138

Across:

1 *Five*
4 *Bard*
8 *Gait* (Five-barred gate)
9 In trouble
11 Entrap
13 Kissing
15 Tongue
16 Talcum
18 Wicket
20 Deject
22 Decided
23 Wrekin
25 Turnstile
26 Maul
27 Hear
28 Door

Down:

2 Iona
3 Earwig
4 Bruise
5 Relent
6 Barracked
7 Stop
10 Engaged
12 Stew
13 Knocked up
14 Subedit
17 Myth
19 Tenure
20 Dinner
21 Jested
23 Wimp
24 Alto

Solutions 139–140

139

Across:
1 Suite
4 Whine (Sweet wine)
10 Wigwams
11 Laugh
12 Ledge
13 Austria
15 Rays
17 Brass
19 Eagle
22 Kiss
25 Possess
27 Safer
29 Enemy
30 Unrolls
31 State
32 Added

Down:
2 Urged
3 Traders
5 Halls
6 Neutral
7 Swell
8 Essay
9 Wheat
14 Uses
16 Asks
18 Respect
20 Assured
21 Speed
23 Issue
24 Press
26 Egypt
28 False

140

Across:
1 Collar
4 Rich (Coleridge)
8 Pummel
9 Admire
10 Mirth
11 Barrier
13 Snip
15 Nil
16 Loot
18 Smashed
20 Bless
23 During
24 Outset
25 Deep
26 Thieve

Down:
1 Caution
2 Limit
3 Ally
5 Immoral
6 Horde
7 Capable
12 Undergo
14 Pastime
17 Obscene
19 Mound
21 Lithe
22 Tosh

Solutions 141–142

141

Across:
1 Massed
4 Apiece (Masterpiece)
7 Theatres
9 Forests
12 Often
13 Drift
15 Litre
16 Onset
17 Drive
18 Naive
19 Session
23 Attitude
24 Growth
25 Ascent

Down:
1 Motionless
2 Spectators
3 Extended
4 Also
5 Idle
6 Cast
8 Efficient
10 Substitute
11 Settlement
14 Toenails
20 Emir
21 Stew
22 Oath

142

Across:
1 Sent
3 Apiece (Centrepiece)
9 Inspect
10 Alibi
11 Err
12 Endowment
13 Delete
14 Staple
16 Maple leaf
19 Rub
21 Icing
22 Marquee
23 Salute
24 Dyke

Down:
1 Seize
2 Nostril
4 Play with fire
5 Exile
6 Epistle
7 Seventy-eight
8 Stud
13 Domains
15 Perjury
17 Phial
18 Emma
20 Breve

Solutions 143-144

143

Across:
1. *Oar*
3. *Din*
5. *Hairy*
8. *Share*
9. *Capitol* (Ordinary share capital)
10. Toil
11. Pastoral
13. Jump up
14. Ice-bag
17. Monoxide
19. Czar
22. In vitro
23. Scorn
24. Auric
25. Sky
26. Few

Down:
1. Onset
2. Realism
3. Deer
4. Nectar
5. Hepatica
6. Inter
7. Yule-log
12. Quixotic
13. Jamaica
15. Buzz off
16. Odious
18. Never
20. Renew
21. Ashy

144

Across:
1. *Stoke*
5. *Mandy*
8. *Ville* (Stoke Mandeville)
9. Ukase
10. Nursemaid
11. Tee
12. Double Dutch
15. Resplendent
19. Rep
20. Groundsel
22. Input
23. Xenon
24. Eject
25. Ghyll

Down:
1. Squatter
2. Okayed
3. Eventual
4. Floral
5. Mete
6. Natant
7. Yard
13. Dwelling
14. Hospital
16. Snooze
17. Nosing
18. Trophy
20. Gale
21. Next

Solutions 145–146

145

Across:
1 Myrrh
4 Curie (Mercury)
8 Sou
9 Needlecraft
10 Oregano
12 Table
13 Impede
14 Splice
17 Paris
19 Alcohol
21 Naphthalene
23 Sat
24 Orate
25 Dodge

Down:
1 Mango
2 Rue
3 Holland
4 Cocoon
5 React
6 Establish
7 Austere
11 Esperanto
13 Impulse
15 Pochard
16 Rattle
18 Sepia
20 Liege
22 End

146

Across:
1 Moor
4 Gauge (Mortgage)
8 Sweet pea
9 Edgy
10 Knit
11 Swansong
12 Centre
14 Ballad
16 Quisling
19 Copy
20 Thai
21 Entrance
22 Royal
23 Yard

Down:
2 Overt
3 Riposte
4 Ghana
5 Utensil
6 Elgin
7 Twinge
13 Testify
14 Bigotry
15 Aspect
17 Usher
18 Ideal
19 Chair

Solutions 147–148

147

Across:
1 Mask
3 Arrayed (Masquerade)
8 Income
9 Valley
10 Grateful
11 Wrap
12 Alarms
15 Yachts
17 Quit
19 Orchards
22 Adjust
23 Tigers
24 Mystery
25 Adds

Down:
1 Minor
2 Shooter
4 Revelry
5 Allow
6 Elegant
7 Reef
13 Laundry
14 Shorter
16 Changed
18 Trust
20 Cite
21 Dares

148

Across:
1 Bred
4 Source (Bread sauce)
7 Rut
9 Jive
10 Original
11 Sew
12 Weed
13 Schmaltz
16 Thunderstruck
19 Freshman
23 Ufos
24 Urn
25 Populist
26 Imps
27 Tot
28 Steely
29 Exit

Down:
2 Raise the roof
3 Dresden
4 Stows
5 Uriah
6 China
8 Fait accompli
14 Circa
15 Mat
17 Doh
18 Reunite
20 Squat
21 Maize
22 Nutty

Solutions 149–150

149

Across:
1 *Begs*
4 *Tee*
6 *Lore*
8 *Borrow* (Beg, steal or borrow)
9 Peptic
10 Thank you
11 Zoom
12 Wheeler-dealer
17 Avid
19 Aquarium
22 Jovial
23 Facile
24 Afar
25 Dud
26 Tate

Down:
2 Epoch
3 Syringe
4 Tawny
5 Expound
6 La Paz
7 Rhizome
10 Tow
13 Hive off
14 Enabled
15 Apricot
16 Ram
18 Drier
20 Unfed
21 Unlit

150

Across:
1 Venice
4 Whaler (Venezuela)
7 Nominate
9 Skipper
12 Tense
13 Rates
15 Filet
16 White
17 Omega
18 Nadal
19 Radical
23 Cytology
24 Always
25 Agreed

Down:
1 Vanity Fair
2 No-man's-land
3 Concerto
4 Week
5 Atop
6 Épée
8 Tsetse fly
10 Palindrome
11 Redeployed
14 Swan song
20 Abel
21 Iowa
22 Acts

Also available from Hamlyn:

Telegraph All New Quick Crosswords £5.99

Volume 2: 978-0-600-62494-3

Volume 3: 978-0-600-62496-7 (publishing in September 2012)

Telegraph All New Big Book of Quick Crosswords £6.99

Volume 1: 978-0-600-62498-1 (publishing in September 2012)

Telegraph All New Toughie Crosswords £5.99

Volume 1: 978-0-600-62502-5

Volume 2: 978-0-600-62495-0 (publishing in September 2012)

Telegraph All New Cryptic Crosswords £5.99

Volume 1: 978-0-600-62468-4

Volume 2: 978-0-600-62500-1

Volume 3: 978-0-600-62499-8 (publishing in September 2012)

Telegraph All New Big Book of Cryptic Crosswords £6.99

Volume 1: 978-0-600-62467-7 (publishing in September 2012)

Telegraph All New Codewords £5.99

Volume 1: 978-0-600-62493-6

Telegraph General Knowledge Crosswords £5.99

Volume 1: 978-0-600-62497-4 (publishing in September 2012)

To order these or other Telegraph Books:

Call: 0844 871 1514
Visit: books.telegraph.co.uk
Post: Send cheques made payable to
Telegraph Books to the following address

Orders Dept
PO Box 582
Norwich
NR7 0GB

All UK orders will be subject to a 99p postage
and packing charge (call for overseas rates).
Products are supplied by and your contract is
with Bertrams Group Ltd not Telegraph Media
Group Limited.

For more puzzles go to
www.puzzles.telegraph.co.uk